Raintree Steck-Vaughn

Illustrated
SCIENCE
ENCYCLOPEDIA
———⟨⊙⟩———

Volume
23

Reference, Bibliography, Index

RSVP

RAINTREE
STECK-VAUGHN
P U B L I S H E R S
The Steck-Vaughn Company

Austin, Texas

Published by Raintree Steck-Vaughn Publishers, an imprint of
Steck-Vaughn Company.

Executive Editor   Diane Sharpe
Senior Editor   Anne Souby
Design Manager   Joyce Spicer

This edition edited and designed by Andromeda Oxford Ltd.

Andromeda Editorial and Design
Project Manager   Julia Roles
Editorial Manager   Jenny Fry
Volume Editor   John Clark
Design   TT Designs, T&S Truscott
Cover Design   John Barker

Library of Congress Cataloging-in-Publication Data
Raintree Steck-Vaughn illustrated science encyclopedia.
          p.   cm.
     Includes bibliographical references and index.
     Summary: A twenty-four volume set containing brief articles
on science topics.
     ISBN 0-8172-3943-X (set)
     ISBN 0-8172-3941-3 (Volume 23)
     1. Science—Encyclopedias, Juvenile.   [1. Science—
Encyclopedias.]   I. Raintree Steck-Vaughn Publishers.
Q121.R354   1997
503—dc20   96-11078
                                        CIP
                                        AC

Printed and Bound in the United States of America.
1 2 3 4 5 6 7 8 9 10 IP 00 99 98 97 96

WRITERS/EDITORS

Jerome J. Ackerman
Val Albrecht
John Andrewartha
Sheila A. Barnett
George M. Bray III
Herta S. Breiter
Anthony J. Castagno
Joseph M. Castagno
Paul G. Cheatham
Michael Chinery
John O. E. Clark
Corinn Codye
Christopher Cooper
Simon de Pinna
Dougal Dixon
Martin Elliott
Paul Q. Fuqua
Stephen R. Gephard
Hope Gilbert
Ian Graham
Richard H. Hauck
Peter Lafferty
Sharon K. Lenninger
Christine Madsen
Moss H. Mendelson
Nina Morgan
William R. Parker
Julian Rowe
Alan Taman
Don Arthur Torgersen
Pam Walton
David M. H. Williams
Paul G. Zomberg

SCIENCE CURRICULUM CONSULTANTS

Virginia "Crickett" Cassara
Indian River County School System

Merrill J. Clark
Rolling Meadows High School
    (retired)

Edith H. Gladden
Philadelphia Regional Introduction
    of Minorities to Engineering

Kathleen A. Gustavson
Nicolet Public High School

Daniel W. Knoebel
Nicolet Public High School

Sheryl Mercier
Fresno Unified School District

F. Joseph Merlino
Philadelphia Renaissance in Science
    and Math

CONTENT ADVISORS
Chemicals and Materials
Dr. Arthur Livermore
Director of Science Education
    (retired)
American Association for the
    Advancement of Science

Earth and the Universe
Dr. Fred Taylor
Institute of Geophysics
The University of Texas at Austin

Health, Medicine, and the
    Human Body
Living Things
How Living Things Function
Dr. Anton Lawson
Arizona State University

Light, Energy, and Motion
Math and Reason
Jennifer Hickman
Boston University Academy

Technology and Society
Michael A. DiSpezio
Science Educational Consultant

SUBJECT CONSULTANTS
Agriculture
Dr. Thomas L. Grady
University of Wisconsin-Madison

Dr. Fred W. Slife
University of Illinois

Anthropology
Dr. Simon Ottenberg
University of Washington

Astronomy/Meteorology
Dr. David H. Menke
Buehler Planetarium
Broward Community College

Craig Robinson
Gengras Planetarium, Children's
    Museum of Hartford

Dr. Louis Winkler
Pennsylvania State University

Biography
Dr. David G. Fenton
Connecticut College

Biology
Merrill J. Clark
Rolling Meadows High School
    (retired)

Dr. E. R. Leadbetter
University of Connecticut

Dr. Carroll R. Norden
University of Wisconsin-
    Milwaukee

Dr. John E. Penick
University of Iowa

Botany
Dr. Marjorie H. Sackett
Amherst College

Chemistry
Dr. Alan Davison
Massachusetts Institute of
    Technology

Dr. Ernest W. Lee
University of North Carolina at
    Greensboro

Dr. John Mellor
University of Bridgeport

Dr. Edward D. Walton
California State Polytechnic
    University

Computer Science
Sarvendra P. Agarwal
Rensselaer Polytechnic Institute

Dr. Bill J. Frye
University of Akron

Earth Science
Daniel W. Knoebel
Nicolet Public High School

Ecology/Zoology
Dr. Robert J. Beyers
University of South Alabama

Elements
Dr. John R. Wilson
Shippensburg State College

Entomology
Jeanne E. Remington
Peabody Museum

General Science
Dr. Glenn D. Berkheimer
Michigan State University

Dr. Geoffrey C. Crockett
Aldrich Chemical Company, Inc.

Geology
Dr. William R. Shirk
Shippensburg State College

Herpetology
Dr. Charles J. Cole
American Museum of Natural History

Richard L. Lattis
New York Zoological Society

Ichthyology
Edward C. Migdalski
Outdoor Education Center,
   Yale University

Industrial Science
Edith H. Gladden
Philadelphia Regional Introduction
   of Minorities to Engineering

F. Joseph Merlino
Philadelphia Renaissance in Science
   and Math

Lower Invertebrates
Dr. Carl S. Hammen
University of Rhode Island

Mammalogy
Dr. John J. Mayer
University of Connecticut

Mathematics
Sarvendra P. Agarwal
Rensselaer Polytechnic
   Institute

Dr. Robert J. Sovchik
University of Akron

Medicine/Anatomy
Dr. Leslie V. Cohen
University of Michigan

Dr. James J. Ferguson
School of Medicine, University of
   Pennsylvania

Dr. Moss H. Mendelson
University of Colorado Health
   Sciences Center

Mineralogy
Dr. Robert Hamilton
Colorado School of Mines

Nutrition
Dr. Leslie O. Schulz
University of Wisconsin-
   Milwaukee

Optics
Dr. Stanley S. Ballard
University of Florida

Ornithology
Mary LeCroy
American Museum of Natural
   History

Dr. Lawrence L. Rauch
California Institute of
   Technology

Dr. Lester L. Short
California Institute of
   Technology

Paleontology
Diane L. Gabriel
Milwaukee Public Museum

Physical Science
Dr. John Daintith
Aylesbury, England, author,
   Introducing Science

Kathleen A. Gustavson
Nicolet Public High School

Dr. Alan Isaacs
Aylesbury, England, author,
   Dictionary of Physical Sciences

Dr. Ernest W. Lee
University of North Carolina at
   Greensboro

Dr. James Tucci
University of Bridgeport

Dr. Edward D. Walton
California State Polytechnic
   University

Dr. Louis Winkler
Pennsylvania State University

Radiological Science
American College of Radiology

Rocketry/Aeronautics
Jesco von Puttkamer
Office of Space Transportation
   Systems

Science Units
Dr. Richard W. Lindquist
Wesleyan University

USING THE RAINTREE STECK-VAUGHN ILLUSTRATED SCIENCE ENCYCLOPEDIA

You are living in a world in which science, technology, and nature are very important. You see something about science almost every day. It might be on television, in the newspaper, in a book at school, or some other place. Often, you want more information about what you see.

The *Raintree Steck-Vaughn Illustrated Science Encyclopedia* will help you find what you want to know. It contains information on many science subjects. You may want to find out about computers, the environment, space exploration, biology, agriculture, or mathematics, for example. They are all in the *Raintree Steck-Vaughn Illustrated Science Encyclopedia.* There are many, many other subjects covered as well.

There are twenty-four volumes in the encyclopedia. The articles, which are called entries, are in alphabetical order through the first twenty-two volumes. On the spine of each volume, below the volume number, are some letters. The letters above the line are the first three letters of the first entry in that volume. The letters below the line are the first three letters of the last entry in that volume. In Volume 1, for example, you see that the first entry begins with **AAR** and that the last entry begins with **ANT**. Using the letters makes it easy to find the volume you need.

In Volume 23, there are three special features—reference charts and tables, a bibliography, and an index. In Volume 24, there are interesting projects that you can do on your own. The projects are fun to do, and they help you discover and understand important science principles. Many can give you ideas that can help you develop your own science fair projects.

Main Entries There are two kinds of main entries in the *Raintree Steck-Vaughn Illustrated Science Encyclopedia.* Many of the entries are major topics that are spread over several pages. The titles of these entries are shown at the top of the page in a yellow box. Other entries required less space to cover the topic fully. The titles of these main entries are printed in capital letters. They look like this: **ABALONE**. At the beginning of some entries, you will see a phonetic pronunciation of the entry title, such as (ăb´ ə lō´ nē).

In the front of each volume, there is a pronunciation key. Use it the same way you use your dictionary's pronunciation key.

Cross-References Within the main entries are cross-references referring to other entries in the encyclopedia. Within an entry, they look like this: (see MAMMAL). At the end of an entry, they look like this: *See also* HYENA. These cross-references tell you where to find other helpful information on the subject you are reading about.

Projects At the end of some entries, you will see this symbol: PROJECT 1. It tells you which projects related to that entry are in Volume 24.

Illustrations There are thousands of photographs, drawings, graphs, diagrams, tables, and other illustrations in the *Raintree Steck-Vaughn Illustrated Science Encyclopedia.* They will help you better understand the entries you read. Captions describe the illustrations. Many of the illustrations also have labels that point out important parts.

Activities Some main entries include activities presented in a special box. These activities are short projects that give you a chance to work with science on your own.

Index In Volume 23, the index lists every main entry by volume and page number. Many subjects that are not main entries are also listed in the index, as well as the illustrations, projects, activities, and reference charts and tables.

Bibliography In Volume 23, there is also a bibliography for students. The books in this list are on a variety of topics and can supplement what you have learned in the *Raintree Steck-Vaughn Illustrated Science Encyclopedia.*

The *Raintree Steck-Vaughn Illustrated Science Encyclopedia* was designed especially for you, the student. It is a source of knowledge for the world of science, technology, and nature. Enjoy it!

PRONUNCIATION KEY

Each symbol has the same sound as the darker letters in the sample words.

ə	balloon, ago	îr	deer, pier	r	root, tire
ă	map, have	j	join, germ	s	so, press
ā	day, made	k	king, ask	sh	shoot, machine
âr	care, bear	l	let, cool	t	to, stand
ä	father, car	m	man, same	th	thin, death
b	ball, rib	n	no, turn	*th*	then, this
ch	choose, nature	ng	bring, long	ŭ	up, cut
d	did, add	ŏ	odd, pot	ûr	urge, hurt
ĕ	bell, get	ō	cone, know	v	view, give
ē	sweet, easy	ô	all, saw	w	wood, glowing
f	fan, soft	oi	boy, boil	y	yes, year
g	good, big	ou	now, loud	z	zero, raise
h	hurt, ahead	o͝o	good, took	zh	leisure, vision
ĭ	rip, ill	o͞o	boot, noon	'	strong accent
ī	side, sky	p	part, scrap	ˏ	weak accent

GUIDE TO MEASUREMENT ABBREVIATIONS

All measurements in the *Raintree Steck-Vaughn Illustrated Science Encyclopedia* are given in both the customary system and the metric system [in brackets like these]. Following are the abbreviations used for various units of measure.

Customary Units of Measure

mi. = miles	cu. yd. = cubic yards
m.p.h. = miles per hour	cu. ft. = cubic feet
yd. = yards	cu. in. = cubic inches
ft. = feet	gal. = gallons
in. = inches	pt. = pints
sq. mi. = square miles	qt. = quarts
sq. yd. = square yards	lb. = pounds
sq. ft. = square feet	oz. = ounces
sq. in. = square inches	fl. oz. = fluid ounces
cu. mi. = cubic miles	°F = degrees Fahrenheit

Metric Units of Measure

km = kilometers	cu. km = cubic kilometers
kph = kilometers per hour	cu. m = cubic meters
m = meters	cu. cm = cubic centimeters
cm = centimeters	ml = milliliters
mm = millimeters	kg = kilograms
sq. km = square kilometers	g = grams
sq. m = square meters	mg = milligrams
sq. cm = square centimeters	°C = degrees Celsius

For information on how to convert customary measurements to metric measurements, see the Metric Conversions table on page 2120 of this volume.

CONTENTS

Metric Conversions

	TO CONVERT	INTO	MULTIPLY BY
Length and distance	inches (in.)	millimeters (mm)	25
	feet (ft.)	centimeters (cm)	30
	yards (yd.)	meters (m)	0.9
	miles (mi.)	kilometers (km)	1.6
	millimeters (mm)	inches (in.)	0.04
	centimeters (cm)	inches (in.)	0.4
	meters (m)	yards (yd.)	1.1
	kilometers (km)	miles (mi.)	0.6
Area	acres	hectares	0.4
	hectares	acres	2.5
Volume and capacity	fluid ounces (fl. oz.)	milliliters (ml)	30
	pints, U.S. (pt.)	liters	0.47
	quarts, U.S. (qt.)	liters	0.95
	gallons, U.S. (gal.)	liters	3.8
	milliliters (ml)	fluid ounces (fl. oz.)	0.034
	liters	pints, U.S. (pt.)	2.1
	liters	quarts, U.S. (qt.)	1.06
	liters	gallons, U.S. (gal.)	0.26
Weight and mass	ounces (oz.)	grams (g)	28
	pounds (lb.)	kilograms (kg)	0.45
	short tons	metric tons	0.9
	grams (g)	ounces (oz.)	0.035
	kilograms (kg)	pounds (lb.)	2.2
	metric tons	short tons	1.1
Temperature	degrees Fahrenheit (°F)	degrees Celsius (°C)	0.555 (after subtracting 32)
	degrees Celsius (°C)	degrees Fahrenheit (°F)	1.8 (then add 32)

Metric Prefixes

Some of the basic metric units are too large or small for everyday measurements. For example, a meter (the metric unit of length) is just over a yard long. To express smaller lengths, scientists use centimeters or millimeters. The prefix "centi-" means a hundredth, and the prefix "milli-" means a thousandth. Lengths or distances larger than a meter are usually stated in kilometers. The prefix "kilo-" means a thousand times.

NAME	NUMBER	FACTOR	PREFIX	SYMBOL
Trillionth	0.000000000001	10^{-12}	pico-	p
Billionth	0.000000001	10^{-9}	nano-	n
Millionth	0.000001	10^{-6}	micro-	μ
Thousandth	0.001	10^{-3}	milli-	m
Hundredth	0.01	10^{-2}	centi-	c
Tenth	0.1	10^{-1}	deci-	d
One	1.0	10^{0}	—	—
Ten	10	10^{1}	deca-	da
Hundred	100	10^{2}	hecto-	h
Thousand	1,000	10^{3}	kilo-	k
Million	1,000,000	10^{6}	mega-	M
Billion	1,000,000,000	10^{9}	giga-	G
Trillion	1,000,000,000,000	10^{12}	tera-	T
Quadrillion	1,000,000,000,000,000	10^{15}	exa-	E

SI Units

The units of measurement used throughout the world of science are called SI units (from *Système Internationale d'Unité*). There are seven basic units, two supplementary units, and eighteen derived units, each with its own symbol.

NAME	SYMBOL	QUANTITY
Basic Units		
meter	m	length
kilogram	kg	mass
second	s	time
kelvin	K	temperature
ampere	A	electric current
mole	mol	amount of substance
candela	cd	luminous intensity
Supplementary Units		
radian	rad	plane angle
steradian	sr	solid angle
Derived Units		
becquerel	Bq	radioactivity
coulomb	C	electric current
farad	F	electric capacitance
gray	Gy	absorbed dose
henry	H	inductance
hertz	Hz	frequency
joule	J	energy
lumen	lm	luminous flux
lux	lx	illuminance
newton	N	force
ohm	Ω	electric resistance
pascal	Pa	pressure
siemens	S	electric conductance
sievert	Sv	dose
tesla	T	magnetic flux density
volt	V	electric potential
watt	W	power
weber	Wb	magnetic flux

Elementary Particles

According to modern atomic theory, all matter is made up of one or more elementary particles—also called fundamental particles. All elementary particles are smaller than an atom, and are therefore also known as subatomic particles. They can be divided into four classes. Baryons react strongly with other particles; gauge bosons act as go-betweens for interactions between two other particles; leptons react weakly with other particles; and mesons help hold particles together in atomic nuclei. Baryons and mesons are made up of even smaller particles called quarks. There are six kinds of quarks (and six kinds of antiquarks), known as up (u), down (d), charm (c), strange (s), top (t), and bottom (b).

TYPE	PARTICLE	MASS	ISOTOPIC SPIN	QUARK CONTENT
Baryons	proton	938.3	$1/2$	uud
	neutron	939.6	$1/2$	udd
	lambda	1,115.6	0	uds
	sigma-plus	1,189.4	1	uus
	sigma-zero	1,192.5	1	uds
	sigma-minus	1,197.4	1	dds
	xi-zero	1,314.9	$1/2$	uss
	xi-minus	1,321.1	$1/2$	dss
	omega-minus	1,672.5	0	sss
	lambda-plus	2,285	0	udc
Gauge bosons	photon	0		
	W-plus/minus	80,000		
	Z-zero	91,000		
Leptons	neutrino	0		
	electron	0.511		
	muon	105.6		
	tauon	1,784		
Mesons	pi-plus/minus	139.6	1	ud, ud
	pi-zero	135.0	1	uu, dd
	K-plus/minus	493.7	$1/2$	us, su
	K-zero	497.7	$1/2$	ds, ds
	eta-zero	548.8	0	uu, dd, ss
	D-plus/minus	1,869.4	$1/2$	cd, dc
	D-zero	1,864.7	$1/2$	cu
	B-plus/minus	5,270.8	$1/2$	ub, bu
	B-zero	5,274.2	$1/2$	db

Periodic Table of the Elements

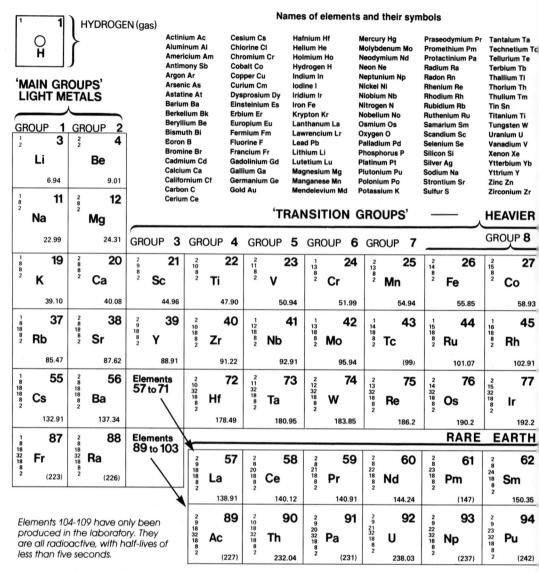

Metals and Nonmetals

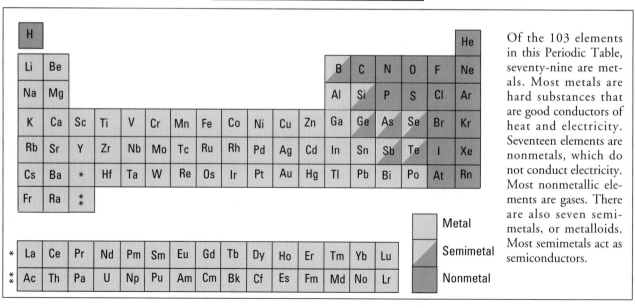

Of the 103 elements in this Periodic Table, seventy-nine are metals. Most metals are hard substances that are good conductors of heat and electricity. Seventeen elements are nonmetals, which do not conduct electricity. Most nonmetallic elements are gases. There are also seven semi-metals, or metalloids. Most semimetals act as semiconductors.

The elements in the same group (vertical column) of the
periodic table are similar to each other, but their properties
gradually change from one end of the group to the other.

number
electrons
each
shell,
later down
inner

2
18
32
18
8
2

80 — atomic number

Hg

200·59

atomic
weight

'MAIN GROUPS'
METALS, 'METALLOIDS,' AND NONMETALS

GROUP 3	GROUP 4	GROUP 5	GROUP 6	GROUP 7	
3 2 — **5** **B** 10.81	4 2 — **6** **C** 12.01	5 2 — **7** **N** 14.01	6 2 — **8** **O** 16.00	7 2 — **9** **F** 19.00	2 — **2** **He** 4.00
3 8 2 — **13** **Al** 26.98	4 8 2 — **14** **Si** 28.09	5 8 2 — **15** **P** 30.97	6 8 2 — **16** **S** 32.06	7 8 2 — **17** **Cl** 35.45	8 2 — **10** **Ne** 20.18
					8 2 — **18** **Ar** 39.95

METALS

GROUP 1   GROUP 2

28 **Ni** 58.71	1 18 8 2 **29** **Cu** 63.54	2 18 8 2 **30** **Zn** 65.37	3 18 8 2 **31** **Ga** 69.72	4 18 8 2 **32** **Ge** 72.59	5 18 8 2 **33** **As** 74.92	6 18 8 2 **34** **Se** 78.96	7 18 8 2 **35** **Br** 79.91	8 18 8 2 **36** **Kr** 83.70
46 **Pd** 106.4	1 18 18 8 2 **47** **Ag** 107.87	2 18 18 8 2 **48** **Cd** 112.40	3 18 18 8 2 **49** **In** 114.82	4 18 18 8 2 **50** **Sn** 118.69	5 18 18 8 2 **51** **Sb** 121.75	6 18 18 8 2 **52** **Te** 127.60	7 18 18 8 2 **53** **I** 126.90	8 18 18 8 2 **54** **Xe** 131.30
78 **Pt** 195.09	1 18 32 18 8 2 **79** **Au** 196.97	2 18 32 18 8 2 **80** **Hg** 200.59	3 18 32 18 8 2 **81** **Tl** 204.37	4 18 32 18 8 2 **82** **Pb** 207.19	5 18 32 18 8 2 **83** **Bi** 208.98	6 18 32 18 8 2 **84** **Po** (210)	7 18 32 18 8 2 **85** **At** (210)	8 18 32 18 8 2 **86** **Rn** (222)

ELEMENTS (ALL TRANSITION GROUP 3)

2 8 25 18 2 **63** **Eu** 151.96	2 9 25 18 2 **64** **Gd** 157.25	2 8 27 18 8 2 **65** **Tb** 158.92	2 8 28 18 8 2 **66** **Dy** 162.50	2 8 29 18 8 2 **67** **Ho** 164.93	2 8 30 18 8 2 **68** **Er** 167.26	2 8 31 18 8 2 **69** **Tm** 168.93	2 8 32 18 8 2 **70** **Yb** 173.04	2 8 32 18 8 2 **71** **Lu** 174.97
2 9 24 32 8 2 **95** **Am** (243)	2 9 25 32 18 8 2 **96** **Cm** (247)	2 9 26 32 18 8 2 **97** **Bk** (249)	2 8 28 32 18 8 2 **98** **Cf** (251)	2 8 29 32 18 8 2 **99** **Es** (254)	2 8 30 32 18 8 2 **100** **Fm** (253)	2 8 31 32 18 8 2 **101** **Md** (256)	2 9 31 32 18 8 2 **102** **No** (254)	2 9 32 32 18 8 2 **103** **Lr** (257)

Common Elements on Earth and in the Body

The most common of the ninety-two elements that occur naturally on the earth is oxygen. This element is also the most common in the human body. Carbon and hydrogen are the next most abundant elements. Figures are percentages.

Name and symbol	Atomic number	% of Earth's crust	% of Earth's atmosphere	% of the human body	Function in the body
Hydrogen H	1	0.14	Trace	9.5	Electron carrier; component of water
Carbon C	6	0.03	0.03	18.5	Backbone of organic molecules
Nitrogen N	7	Trace	78.1	3.3	Component of all nucleic acids and proteins
Oxygen O	8	46.6	20.95	65.0	Required for cellular respiration; component of water
Fluorine F	9	0.07	–	Trace	
Sodium Na	11	2.8	–	0.2	Important in nerve functioning
Magnesium Mg	12	2.1	–	0.1	Component of many energy-transferring enzymes
Aluminum Al	13	8.1	–	Trace	
Silicon Si	14	27.7	–	Trace	
Phosphorus P	15	0.07	–	1.0	Backbone of nucleic acids; component of bones and teeth
Sulfur S	16	0.03	–	0.3	Component of some proteins
Chlorine Cl	17	0.01	–	0.2	Negative ion bathing cells
Potassium K	19	2.6	–	0.4	Important in nerve functioning
Calcium Ca	20	3.6	–	1.5	Component of bones and teeth
Manganese Mn	25	0.1	–	Trace	
Iron Fe	26	5.0	–	Trace	Component of hemoglobin in blood

Some Properties and Uses of Elements

ELEMENT	SYMBOL	IMPORTANT PROPERTIES	USES
Actinium	Ac	Radioactive	Production of neutrons
Aluminum	Al	Thin; light; good heat conductor	Pots and pans; bodies of vehicles; packaging; wires
Americium	Am	Human-made; radioactive; superconductive	Mainly research
Antimony	Sb	Hard	Hardens and strengthens lead
Argon	Ar	Nonreactive	Electric light bulbs
Arsenic	As	Brittle; poisonous	Insecticides and herbicides
Astatine	At	Occurs naturally in very small amounts; radioactive	Research only
Barium	Ba	Reacts readily with oxygen	Ceramics; glass; purifies certain chemical solutions
Berkelium	Bk	Human-made; radioactive	Research only
Beryllium	Be	Poisonous; light; absorbs heat	Spacecraft
Bismuth	Bi	Melts at low temperatures when mixed with certain metals	Automatic sprinkler systems
Boron	B	Absorbs neutrons without being changed by them	Nuclear reactor control rods
Bromine	Br	Heavy; strong irritating odor	Photographic film
Cadmium	Cd	Poisonous; silvery white	Coats metals
Calcium	Ca	Reacts slowly with water	Necessary for bone and teeth growth; plaster
Californium	Cf	Human-made; radioactive	To locate gold and silver
Carbon	C	Three forms: amorphous carbon, diamond, graphite	Jewelry; cutting tools; heating
Cerium	Ce	Abundant; electron structure easily changed	Strengthens alloys
Cesium	Cs	Ionizes readily when heated or struck with light	Electronic tubes; photoelectric cells
Chlorine	Cl	Poisonous; bleaches	Bleaching powders and fluids; industrial chemicals for cooling
Chromium	Cr	Resists corrosion; becomes shiny when polished	Coats metals; hardens steel
Cobalt	Co	Very magnetic	Alloys made into magnet
Copper	Cu	Conducts electricity well; malleable	Cooking utensils; wires for telephone systems
Curium	Cm	Human-made; radioactive	Research only
Dysprosium	Dy	Forms yellowish green salts	Research only
Einsteinium	Es	Human-made; radioactive	Research only
Erbium	Er	Forms rose-colored salts	Pink glass
Europium	Eu	Produces the color red when combined with other compounds	Color televisions
Fermium	Fm	Human-made; radioactive	Mainly research
Fluorine	F	Readily reacts with other elements	Compounds used to fight tooth decay and as coolants
Francium	Fr	Occurs naturally in very small amounts; radioactive	Research only
Gadolinium	Gd	Strongly magnetic at room temperature but loses its magnetism when heated slightly	Control rods of nuclear reactors
Gallium	Ga	Conducts electricity well	Transistors; memory devices in computers
Germanium	Ge	Good semiconductor	Diodes; solar batteries
Gold	Au	Scarce; resists chemicals; malleable	Jewelry; dentistry; electrical circuits
Hafnium	Hf	Resists corrosion; absorbs neutrons well	Control rods of nuclear reactors
Helium	He	Light; very unreactive	Rocket fuel; lifts balloons; prevents chemicals from reacting with other elements during storage and transportation
Holmium	Ho	Silver in color	Research only
Hydrogen	H	Very abundant; reactive; light; extremely flammable	Fuel; compounds found in many foods and water
Indium	In	Rare; soft	Coats bearings in high-speed engines; transistors
Iodine	I	Antiseptic; causes the production of hormones in the human body	Human growth; chemical analysis; compounds are mild antiseptics
Iridium	Ir	Dense; hard	Machine bearings; electrical contacts
Iron	Fe	Magnetic; essential part of hemoglobin (a substance in human blood)	Electrical devices; helps blood carry oxygen from the lungs to the body
Krypton	Kr	Nonreactive	Electronic tubes
Lanthanum	La	Reacts readily with oxygen	Camera lenses
Lawrencium	Lr	Human-made; radioactive	Research only
Lead	Pb	Soft; resists corrosion	Electric batteries
Lithium	Li	Very light and reactive	Ceramics; glass; electric batteries
Lutetium	Lu	Very heavy	Catalyst in chemical industry
Magnesium	Mg	Light; reactive	Vehicle parts; protects steel from corrosion; flares; flashbulbs
Manganese	Mn	Hard and brittle	Hardens steel; catalyst
Mendelevium	Md	Human-made; radioactive	Research only

ELEMENT	SYMBOL	IMPORTANT PROPERTIES	USES
Mercury	Hg	Only metal that is liquid at room temperature	Barometers; thermometers; lamps
Molybdenum	Mo	Hard	Vehicle parts; cutting tools
Neodymium	Nd	Becomes rose-colored when combined with elements	Lasers; ceramics; glass
Neon	Ne	Nonreactive	Lamps; luminous tubes
Neptunium	Np	Rare; radioactive	Detects neutrons
Nickel	Ni	Slightly magnetic; resists corrosion	Protective coating; added to iron to make it resistant to corrosion
Niobium	Nb	Can withstand high temperatures; superconducting at low temperatures	Cores of nuclear reactors; superconducting magnets
Nitrogen	N	Abundant in air; important part of protein molecule	Essential element of life; quick-freezes foods; produces ammonia for fertilizer
Nobelium	No	Human-made; radioactive	Research only
Osmium	Os	Very hard	Electrical parts; bearings; pen points
Oxygen	O	Life-supporting gas; very reactive	Part of respiration in plants and animals; combines with other elements to form rocket fuel
Palladium	Pd	Very absorbent	Catalyst; wire; jewelry; dentistry
Phosphorus	P	White phosphorus is poisonous and very reactive; red phosphorus is not poisonous and less reactive	Fertilizers
Platinum	Pt	Hard; resists heat and other chemicals	Surgical instruments; electrodes; jewelry
Plutonium	Pu	Radioactive; explosive	Energy source in nuclear weapons and reactors
Polonium	Po	Radioactive	Source of neutrons
Potassium	K	Very soft; reacts readily with oxygen and water	Fertilizer; involved in the sending of messages by nerves in the human body
Praseodymium	Pr	Dissolves to form a green solution or salt	Ceramics; glass
Promethium	Pm	Human-made; radioactive	Source of beta particles
Protactinium	Pa	Radioactive	Research only
Radium	Ra	Radioactive	Research only
Radon	Rn	Radioactive	Research only
Rhenium	Re	Can withstand high temperatures; hard	Catalyst; electrical contacts
Rhodium	Rh	Hard; resists corrosion	Catalyst; coats jewelry; electrical contacts
Rubidium	Rb	Bursts into flames when placed in air or water	Catalyst; vacuum tubes
Ruthenium	Ru	Hard; does not dissolve in water or acids	Hardens platinum and palladium
Samarium	Sm	Magnetic	Catalyst; magnets
Scandium	Sc	Soft	Research only
Selenium	Se	Conducts electricity when light shines on it	Photoelectric cells
Silicon	Si	Reactive; good semiconductor	Transistors; solar cells
Silver	Ag	Soft; good electrical conductor	Jewelry; tableware; food-processing equipment
Sodium	Na	Soft; reactive; good electrical conductor	Coating for wires; fertilizer; soaps
Strontium	Sr	Radioactive; its salts give a red color to flames	Fireworks; flares
Sulfur	S	Reactive	Wood and rubber industries; matches
Tantalum	Ta	Compounds are efficient insulators	Capacitors
Technetium	Tc	Radioactive	Research only
Tellurium	Te	When combined with other elements, it hardens them and increases their resistance to corrosion	Alloy; semiconductors
Terbium	Tb	Its compounds glow with a green color	Color televisions; lasers
Thallium	Tl	Soft; poisonous	Insecticides; poisons
Thorium	Th	Radioactive	Photoelectric cells; potential fuel source for nuclear reactors
Thulium	Tm	Radioactive	X-ray machines
Tin	Sn	Resists corrosion	Cans; coating on products to make resistant to corrosion
Titanium	Ti	Light; strong; resists corrosion	Aircraft and ship bodies; propellers
Tungsten	W	Resists corrosion	Electric light bulbs; cutting tools
Uranium	U	Radioactive	Fuel for nuclear reactors
Vanadium	V	Hard	Strengthens steel
Xenon	Xe	Nonreactive	Electron tubes
Ytterbium	Yb	Soft; silvery	Chemical experiments
Yttrium	Y	Compounds are phosphorescent	Color televisions; lasers
Zinc	Zn	Resists corrosion	Coats metals and steel; electric batteries
Zirconium	Zr	Resists corrosion; does not readily absorb neutrons	Cores of nuclear reactors; furnace linings

Common Chemicals

Many chemicals in everyday use are still known to non-chemists by their old common names, some dating back hundreds of years. This table gives the modern scientific names of some of these chemicals, along with their uses. Many common chemicals are corrosive or poisonous and should be handled only with great care.

COMMON NAME	CHEMICAL NAME	COMMON USES
Alum	Aluminum potassium sulfate	Dyeing, tanning, leather finishing, paper sizing, styptic
Baking soda	Sodium hydrogen carbonate	Antacid, cooking, fire extinguishers, paper making, tanning
Blackboard chalk	Calcium sulfate	Chalk, manufacture of ceramics, paint, sulfuric acid
Black lead	Graphite	Metal polish, lubricant, pencils, electrical contacts
Blue vitriol	Copper(II) sulfate	Fungicide, timber preservation, electroplating, dyeing
Borax	Disodium tetraborate	Ant killer, flux, glass making, antiseptic
Butter of zinc	Zinc chloride	Solder flux, dehydrating agent, catalyst, dry batteries
Calamine	Zinc carbonate	Powder or lotion to treat sunburn and skin disorders
Caustic potash	Potassium hydroxide	Soap making, batteries, absorbing acid gases
Caustic soda	Sodium hydroxide	Drain cleaner, making soap, paper, aluminum, petrochemicals
Chinese white	Zinc oxide	Pigment, skin ointment, making ceramics, plastics
Common salt	Sodium chloride	Seasoning, food preserving, making sodium carbonate and hydroxide
Cream of tartar	Potassium hydrogen tartrate	Baking powder, acidity-controlling food additive
Epsom salt(s)	Magnesium sulfate	Laxative, fireproofing fabrics, tanning, making fertilizers, matches
Glauber's salts	Sodium sulfate	Laxative, making glass, wood pulp, dyeing
Glycol	Ethane-1, 2-diol	Antifreezes, coolants, making polyester fibers and plasticizers
Green vitriol	Iron(II) sulfate	Anemia treatment, tanning, making inks
Hypo	Sodium thiosulfate	Fixing in photography, dyeing, preventing fermentation
Jeweler's rouge	Iron(III) oxide	Abrasive, pigment
Killed spirits of salt	Zinc chloride	Solder flux, dehydrating agent, catalyst, dry batteries
Lamp black	Carbon	Pigment, filler for rubber in vehicle tires
Lime	Calcium oxide	Gardening, making glass, paper, steel
Metaldehyde	Ethanal tetramer	Camping fuel, slug killer
Milk of magnesia	Magnesium hydroxide	Antacid, refractory, heat insulation, reflective coatings
Mineral chalk	Calcium carbonate	Making lime and sodium carbonate
Plaster of Paris	Calcium sulfate	Casts and molds, pottery, builder's plaster
Plumbago	Graphite	Metal polish, lubricant, pencils, electrical contacts
Potash	Potassium carbonate	Fertilizer, dyeing, wood finishing, glass, soap
Prussian blue	Iron(III) hexacyanoferrate(II)	Pigment
Sal ammoniac	Ammonium chloride	Flashlight batteries, treatment of textile fibers, galvanizing flux
Sal volatile	Ammonium carbonate	Smelling salts, baking powders, wool finishing, expectorant
Slaked lime	Calcium hydroxide	Gardening, water treatment, making mortar, bleaching powder
Soda ash	Anhydrous sodium carbonate	Glass making, food additive, photography, textile treatment
Soda water	Carbonic acid	Soft drink
Vinegar	Diluteacetic (ethanoic) acid	Flavoring, pickling agent
Washing soda	Sodium carbonate	Cleanser, glass making, photography, textile treatment
Water glass	Sodium silicate	Sizing, making silica gel (drying agent)

Physical Properties of Common Metals

The densest metals are osmium, iridium, and platinum. These are all rare metals with special uses. The least dense metal is lithium, which has only half the density of water. There is also a wide range of melting points among metals. Mercury has the lowest melting point and is a liquid at ordinary temperatures. The solid metal with the lowest melting point is cesium. Tungsten has both the highest melting point and the highest boiling point. Chromium is the hardest metal, and cesium is the softest. Like sodium and potassium, cesium can easily be cut with a knife.

	RELATIVE DENSITY	MELTING POINT (°F)	MELTING POINT (°C)	BOILING POINT (°F)	BOILING POINT (°C)	HARDNESS (MOHS SCALE)
Aluminum	2.7	1,200	600	4,472	2,467	2–2.9
Barium	3.5	1,337	725	2,984	1,640	
Beryllium	1.85	2,352	1,289	4,482	2,472	
Bismuth	9.8	520	271	2,840	1,560	2.5
Cadmium	8.65	610	321	1,413	767	2.0
Calcium	1.5	1,542	839	2,703	1,484	1.5
Cesium	1.9	83.1	28.4	1,240	671	0.2
Chromium	7.2	3,452	1,900	4,874	2,690	9.0
Cobalt	8.9	2,723	1,495	5,621	3,100	
Copper	1.5	1,981	1,083	4,652	2,567	2.5–3
Gallium	5.9	85.6	29.8	4,001	2,205	1.5
Germanium	5.5	1,756	958	5,162	2,850	
Gold	19.3	1,945	1,063	4,820	2,660	2.5–3
Hafnium	13.3	4,404	2,227	8,317	4,603	
Iridium	22.4	4,437	2,447	8,002	4,428	6–6.5
Iron	7.86	2,759	1,535	5,437	3,000	4–5
Lead	11.34	621.5	327.5	3,182	1,750	1.5
Lithium	0.53	356	180	2,456	1,347	0.6
Magnesium	1.7	1,200	649	1,994	1,090	2.0
Manganese	7.2	2,275	1,246	3,744	2,062	5.0
Mercury	13.5	-38	-39	675	357	
Molybdenum	10.2	4,753	2,623	8,382	4,639	
Nickel	8.9	2,647	1,453	4,950	2,732	
Osmium	22.48	5,491	3,033	9,054	5,012	7.0
Palladium	12.02	2,831	1,555	5,367	2,964	4.8
Platinum	21.5	3,222	1,772	6,900	3,800	4.3
Plutonium	19.8	1,184	640	6,260	3,460	
Potassium	0.86	146	63	1,410.8	766	0.5
Radium	5.0	1,290	700	2,080	1,140	
Rhodium	12.1	3,565	1,963	6,687	3,697	
Rubidium	1.48	103.1	39.5	1,270	688	0.3
Selenium	4.45	430	221	1,265	685	2.0
Silver	10.5	1,762	961	3,956	2,193	2.5–4
Sodium	0.97	208	98	1,621	881	0.4
Strontium	2.6	1,416	769	2,520	1,382	1.8
Tantalum	16.6	5,468	3,020	9,856	5,458	
Tin	7.3	482	250	4,717	2,603	1.5–1.8
Titanium	4.5	3,033	1,667	5,949	3,287	
Tungsten	19.3	6,170	3,400	10,220	5,600	
Uranium	19.0	2,070	1,132	6,904	3,818	
Vanadium	5.96	3,470	1,910	6,168	3,409	
Zinc	7.14	787.24	419.6	1,664.6	907	2.5
Zirconium	6.5	3,371	1,855	7,968	4,409	

Geological Time Scale

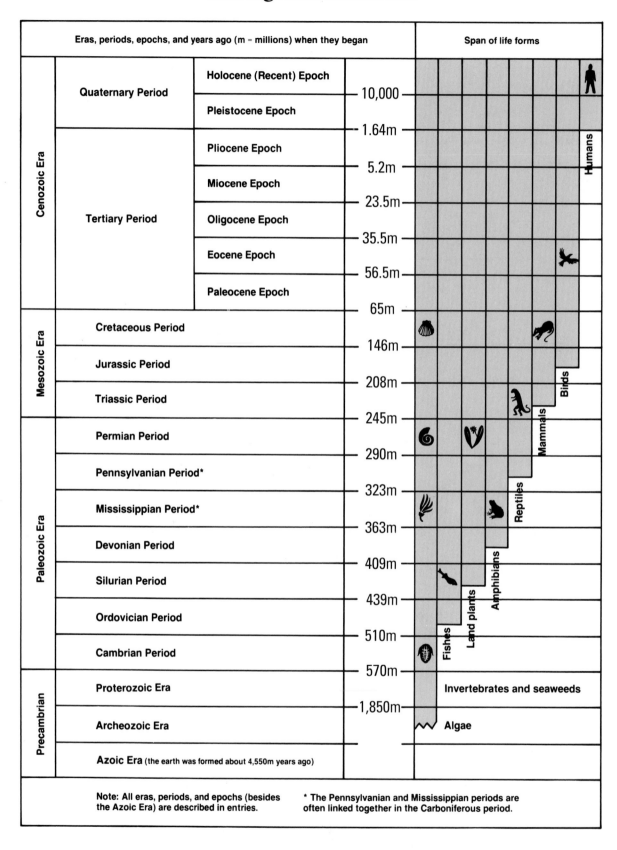

Eras, periods, epochs, and years ago (m = millions) when they began				Span of life forms
Cenozoic Era	**Quaternary Period**	Holocene (Recent) Epoch		Humans
			10,000	
		Pleistocene Epoch		
	Tertiary Period	Pliocene Epoch	1.64m	
			5.2m	
		Miocene Epoch		
			23.5m	
		Oligocene Epoch		
			35.5m	
		Eocene Epoch		
			56.5m	
		Paleocene Epoch		
			65m	
Mesozoic Era	**Cretaceous Period**			
			146m	Birds
	Jurassic Period			
			208m	Mammals
	Triassic Period			
			245m	Reptiles
Paleozoic Era	**Permian Period**			
			290m	
	Pennsylvanian Period*			
			323m	Amphibians
	Mississippian Period*			
			363m	
	Devonian Period			Land plants
			409m	
	Silurian Period			Fishes
			439m	
	Ordovician Period			
			510m	
	Cambrian Period			
			570m	
Precambrian	**Proterozoic Era**			Invertebrates and seaweeds
			1,850m	
	Archeozoic Era			Algae
	Azoic Era (the earth was formed about 4,550m years ago)			

Note: All eras, periods, and epochs (besides the Azoic Era) are described in entries.

* The Pennsylvanian and Mississippian periods are often linked together in the Carboniferous period.

World Data

The World and the Continents

	AREA	
	(SQ. MI.)	(SQ. KM)
The World	196,698,640	509,450,000
Land	57,702,645	149,450,000
Water	139,000,000	360,000,000
Asia	17,181,450	44,500,000
Africa	11,699,600	30,302,000
North America	9,359,450	24,241,000
South America	6,869,880	17,793,000
Antarctica	5,444,000	14,100,000
Europe	3,844,400	9,957,000
Australia and Oceania	3,303,860	8,557,000

Oceans and Seas

NAME	AREA	
	(SQ. MI.)	(SQ. KM)
Pacific Ocean	69,375,000	179,679,000
Atlantic Ocean	35,665,000	92,373,000
Indian Ocean	28,539,000	73,917,000
Arctic Ocean	5,440,000	14,090,000
Caribbean Sea	1,068,000	2,766,000
Mediterranean Sea	971,430	2,516,000
South China Sea	894,980	2,318,000
Bering Sea	875,675	2,268,000
Gulf of Mexico	595,750	1,543,000
Sea of Okhotsk	589,961	1,528,000
East China and Yellow Sea	482,240	1,249,000
Hudson Bay	475,675	1,232,000
Sea of Japan	389,190	1,008,000
North Sea	222,010	575,000
Black Sea	174,520	452,000
Red Sea	169,110	438,000

Lakes

NAME	AREA	
	(SQ. MI.)	(SQ. KM)
Caspian Sea	143,240	371,000
Lake Superior	31,740	82,200
Lake Victoria	26,255	68,000
Lake Huron	23,010	59,600
Lake Michigan	22,390	58,000
Aral Sea	13,900	36,000
Lake Tanganyika	12,740	33,000
Great Bear Lake	12,160	31,500
Lake Baikal	12,160	31,500
Lake Malawi/ Nyasa	11,200	29,000

Rivers

NAME	LOCATION OF MOUTH	LENGTH (MI.)	(KM)
Nile	Mediterranean Sea	4,145	6,670
Amazon	Atlantic Ocean	3,995	6,430
Yangtze	East China Sea	3,965	6,380
Mississippi/ Missouri	Gulf of Mexico	3,740	6,020
Yenisei/Angara	Kara Sea	3,450	5,550
Ob/Irtysh	Gulf of Ob	3,360	5,410
Huang He	Yellow Sea	3,010	4,840
Zaire/Congo	Atlantic Ocean	2,900	4,670
Amur	Sea of Okhotsk	2,800	4,510
Mekong	South China Sea	2,795	4,500

Islands

NAME	AREA	
	(SQ. MI.)	(SQ. KM)
Greenland	839,999	2,175,600
New Guinea	301,158	780,000
Borneo	284,556	737,000
Madagascar	226,640	587,000
Baffin Island	196,139	508,000
Sumatra	164,092	425,000
Honshu	88,803	230,000
Great Britain	88,757	229,880
Victoria Island	81,930	212,200

Mountains

NAME	LOCATION	HEIGHT (FT.)	(M)
Everest	China/Nepal	29,029	8,848
Godwin Austen (K2)	China/Kashmir	28,251	8,611
Kanchenjunga	India/Nepal	28,208	8,598
Lhotse	China/Nepal	27,939	8,516
Makalu	China/Nepal	27,824	8,481
Dhaulagiri	Nepal	26,811	8,172
Manaslu	Nepal	26,758	8,156
Cho Oyu	China/Nepal	26,750	8,151
Nanga Parbat	Kashmir	26,660	8,126
Annapurna	Nepal	26,502	8,078

Solar System

Mercury Venus Earth Mars

Jupiter

Planetary Data

PLANET	DISTANCE FROM SUN IN AU*	DIAMETER (EARTH = 1)	MASS (EARTH = 1)	TIME OF 1 ROTATION (H = HOURS, M = MINUTES)
Mercury	0.4	0.38	0.05	58.6 days
Venus	0.7	0.95	0.81	243 days
Earth	1.0	1.00	1.00	23H, 56M
Mars	1.5	0.53	0.10	24H, 37M
Jupiter	5.2	11.19	317.9	9H, 55M
Saturn	9.5	9.36	95.2	10H, 14M
Uranus	19.2	4.06	14.6	17H
Neptune	30.1	3.88	17.2	22H
Pluto	39.4	0.21	0.0017	6.4 days

*AU means astronomical unit. Earth is 1 AU from the sun.

PLANET	TIME OF 1 REVOLUTION (IN YEARS)	DENSITY* (in g/cu. cm)	NUMBER OF KNOWN SATELLITES
Mercury	0.2	5.5	0
Venus	0.6	5.2	0
Earth	1.0	5.5	1
Mars	1.9	3.9	2
Jupiter	11.8	1.3	16
Saturn	29.4	0.7	23
Uranus	84.0	1.2	15
Neptune	164.8	1.6	8
Pluto	248.4	4.5	1

* The density of water is 1 g/cu. cm, or 1 gram per cubic centimeter.

Asteroids

NUMBER	NAME	DATE FOUND	DISTANCE FROM SUN (AU.)* MIN.	MAX.	SIDEREAL PERIOD (YR.)	DIAMETER (MI.)	(KM)
1	Ceres	1801	2.55	2.94	4.60	623	1,003
2	Pallas	1802	2.11	3.42	4.60	332	535
3	Juno	1804	1.98	3.35	4.36	155	250
4	Vesta	1807	2.15	2.57	3.63	311	500
5	Astrea	1845	2.10	3.06	4.14	112	180
6	Hebe	1847	1.93	2.92	3.78	121	195
7	Iris	1847	1.84	2.94	3.69	130	209
8	Flora	1847	1.86	2.55	3.27	94	151
9	Metis	1848	2.09	2.68	3.68	94	151
10	Hygeia	1849	2.84	3.46	5.59	267	430

* AU means astronomical unit. Earth is 1 AU from the sun.

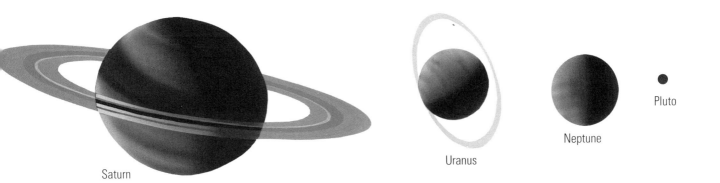

Saturn Uranus Neptune Pluto

Moons of Planets

NAME OF MOON	DISTANCE FROM PLANET (MI.)	(KM)	ORBITAL PERIOD (DAYS)	NAME OF MOON	DISTANCE FROM PLANET (MI.)	(KM)	ORBITAL PERIOD (DAYS)
Earth				Dione	234,270	377,000	2.737
Moon	238,861	384,392	27.32	Helene	234,270	377,000	2.737
				Rhea	327,500	527,040	4.518
Mars				Titan	758,700	1,221,000	15.945
Phobos	5,760	9,270	0.319	Hyperion	920,360	1,481,100	21.277
Deimos	14,600	23,500	1.2624	Iapetus	2,213,000	3,561,300	79.331
				Phoebe	8,050,000	12,954,000	550.4
Jupiter							
Metis	79,510	127,960	0.295	**Uranus**			
Adrastea	80,150	128,980	0.298	Cordelia	30,740	49,471	0.330
Amalthea	112,660	181,300	0.498	Ophelia	33,430	53,796	0.372
Thebe	137,890	221,900	0.675	Bianca	36,770	59,173	0.433
Io	261,200	421,600	1.769	Cressida	38,390	61,777	0.463
Europa	416,960	671,000	3.551	Desdemona	38,950	62,676	0.475
Ganymede	664,900	1,070,000	7.12	Juliet	39,990	64,352	0.493
Callisto	1,118,500	1,800,000	16.689	Portia	41,065	66,085	0.513
Leda	6,893,800	11,094,000	238.7	Rosalind	43,460	69,941	0.558
Himalia	7,133,700	11,480,000	250.6	Belinda	46,765	75,258	0.622
Lysithea	7,282,800	11,720,000	259.2	Puck	53,440	86,000	0.762
Elara	7,293,400	11,737,000	259.7	Miranda	80,410	129,400	1.414
Ananke	13,174,000	21,200,000	631	Ariel	80,780	130,000	2.520
Carme	14,044,000	22,600,000	692	Umbriel	165,290	266,000	4.144
Pasiphaë	14,603,000	23,500,000	735	Titania	362,520	583,400	8.706
Sinope	14,727,000	23,700,000	758	Oberon	362,520	583,400	13.463
Saturn				**Neptune**			
Pan	83,020	133,600	0.58	Naiad	29,950	48,200	0.30
Atlas	85,550	137,670	0.602	Thalassa	31,070	50,000	0.31
Prometheus	86,590	139,350	0.613	Galatea	32,620	52,500	0.33
Pandora	88,050	141,700	0.629	Despina	38,525	62,000	0.40
Epimetheus	94,090	151,420	0.694	Larissa	45,735	73,600	0.56
Janus	94,120	151,470	0.695	Proteus	73,075	117,600	1.12
Mimas	115,290	185,540	0.942	Triton	220,470	354,800	5.877
Enceladus	147,920	238,040	1.370	Nereid	3,426,025	5,513,400	365.2
Tethys	183,130	294,700	1.888				
Telesto	183,110	294,670	1.888	**Pluto**			
Calypso	183,110	294,670	1.888	Charon	12,430	20,000	6.4

Space Probes

YEAR	NATION	CRAFT	RESULT
Moon			
1959	USSR	Luna 1	Bypasses moon
		Luna 2	Impacts on moon
		Luna 3	Bypasses, photographs far side
1962	USA	Ranger 4	Crash-lands on far side
1965	USA	Rangers 7–9	Takes photographs before crash-landing
	USSR	Zond 3	Bypasses, photographs far side
1966	USSR	Luna 9	First soft landing, takes photographs
	USSR	Luna 10	First lunar orbiter
	USA	Surveyor 1	Soft landing, takes photographs
	USSR	Luna 11	Lunar orbiter
	USA	Lunar Orbiter 1	Detailed photographs of far side
	USA	Lunar Orbiter 2	Photographs surface
	USSR	Luna 13	Soft landing, studies rocks
1967	USA	Lunar Orbiter 3	Photographs surface
	USA	Surveyor 3	Soft landing, photographs surface
	USA	Lunar Orbiter 4	Photographs surface
	USA	Surveyor 5	Soft landing, studies soil
	USA	Surveyor 6	Soft landing
1968	USA	Surveyor 7	Soft landing; last unmanned U.S. probe
	USSR	Zond 5	Flies around moon and back
	USSR	Zond 6	Flies around moon and back
	USA	Apollo 8	Manned orbits of moon and back
1969	USA	Apollo 9	Lander tested in Earth orbit
	USSR	Luna 15	Soft landing
	USA	Apollo 10	Lander tested in moon orbit
	USA	Apollo 11	First manned landing
	USA	Apollo 12	Second manned landing
1970	USA	Apollo 13	Recalled from moon orbit
	USSR	Luna 16	Returns with rock samples
	USSR	Luna 17	Lands Lunakhod 1 moon rover
1971	USA	Apollo 14	Third manned landing
	USA	Apollo 15	Fourth landing, lands Lunar Rover
1972	USA	Apollo 16	Fifth manned landing
	USA	Apollo 17	Sixth (last) manned landing
1994	USA	Clementine	Moon mapping from orbit
Mercury			
1974	USA	Mariner 10	Two bypasses, takes photographs
1975	USA	Mariner 10	Makes third bypass
Venus			
1961	USSR	Venera 1	Contact lost, bypasses planet
1962	USA	Mariner 2	Bypasses planet
1966	USSR	Venera 2	
	USSR	Venera 3	Lander
1967	USSR	Venera 4	Drops instruments in atmosphere
	USA	Mariner 5	Close bypass
1969	USSR	Venera 5	
	USSR	Venera 6	
1970	USSR	Venera 7	Soft landing
1971	USSR	Venera 8	Soft landing
1974	USA	Mariner 10	Bypasses planet
1975	USSR	Venera 9	Soft landing, photographs
	USSR	Venera 10	Soft landing, photographs
1978	USA	Pioneer Venus 1	Makes radar maps of planet
	USA	Pioneer Venus 2	Launches atmospheric probes

Space Probes (continued)

YEAR	NATION	CRAFT	RESULT
(Venus continued)			
1980	USSR	Venera 11	Lander, analyzes atmosphere
	USSR	Venera 12	Lander, analyzes atmosphere
1982	USSR	Venera 13	Soft landing, examines rocks
	USSR	Venera 14	Soft landing
1983	USSR	Venera 15	Orbits, radar maps of surface
1984	USSR	Venera 16	Orbits, radar maps of surface
1985	USSR	Vega 1	Bypasses en route to Halley's comet
	USSR	Vega 2	Bypasses en route to Halley's comet
1990	USA	Magellan	Radar maps surface
Mars			
1962	USSR	Mars 1	Contact lost March 1963
1965	USA	Mariner 4	Bypasses planet, photographs
1969	USA	Mariner 6	
	USA	Mariner 7	
1971	USA	Mariner 8	Failed
	USA	Mariner 9	Orbits planet
	USSR	Mars 2	Orbits planet
	USSR	Mars 3	Lands, contact soon lost
	USA	Mariner 9	Orbits planet
1974	USSR	Mars 4	Lander
	USSR	Mars 5	
	USSR	Mars 6	
	USSR	Mars 7	
1976	USA	Viking 1	Soft landing, photographs
	USA	Viking 2	Soft landing, photographs
1993	USA	Orbiter	Loses contact when entering orbit
Asteroid Belt			
1991	USA	Galileo	Photographs Gaspra
1993	USA	Galileo	Photographs Ida
Jupiter			
1973	USA	Pioneer 10	Bypasses planet
1974	USA	Pioneer 11	Bypasses planet
1979	USA	Voyager 1, 2	Bypass planet, discover ring
1995	USA	Galileo	Tours Jupiter's moons
Saturn			
1979	USA	Pioneer 11	Bypasses planet
1980	USA	Voyager 1	Bypasses planet, finds moons
1981	USA	Voyager 2	Bypasses planet
Uranus			
1986	USA	Voyager 2	Bypasses planet, finds moons
Neptune			
1989	USA	Voyager 2	Bypasses planet
Halley's Comet			
1986	USA	ICE	Bypasses comet; no useful data
	USSR	Vega 1	Bypasses comet; no useful data
	USSR	Vega 2	Bypasses comet; no useful data
	Japan	Sakigake	Bypasses comet; no useful data
	Europe	Giotto	Passes within 370 mi. [600 km] of nucleus
	Japan	Suisei	Bypasses comet

Classification—The Five Kingdoms

The five-kingdom system of classification is the most widely accepted by biologists today. It divides all living organisms into the kingdoms Monera (bacteria and cyanobacteria, or blue-green algae), Fungi (mushrooms and molds), Plantae (many-celled plants), Animalia (many-celled animals), and Protista (all organisms that do not belong to any of the other kingdoms). Kingdoms are subdivided into phyla (plural of *phylum*), sometimes called divisions in the plant kingdom. Phyla are made up of a number of classes, and classes are in turn comprised of orders, containing families of several genera (plural of *genus*). Monera are the simplest organisms, consisting of single cells called prokaryotes. The cells have no nucleus. The cells of all other organisms do have nuclei and are called eukaryotes.

KINGDOM MONERA
Prokaryotic cells
  Bacteria and cyanobacteria (blue-green algae)

KINGDOM PROTISTA
All creatures that do not fall into the other four kingdoms. There is no phylogenetic relationship between these. The protista include:
  Slime molds
  Oomycetes
  Dinoflagellates
  Various kinds of algae (excluding the blue-green algae, but including euglenoids, diatoms, and various seaweeds)
  Former members of the Protozoans, including foraminiferans, radiolarians, ciliates, amebas

KINGDOM FUNGI
Eukaryotes that never have flagella or cilia at any stage of the life cycle, that produce spores, and that lack embryological development.

KINGDOM PLANTAE
Photosynthetic eukaryotes that develop from embryos and show an alteration between haploid and diploid generations in their life cycles.
  Mosses, liverworts, hornworts
  Ferns, club mosses, horsetails
  Cycads, ginkgoes, conifers
  Angiosperms, or flowering plants
See pages 2136–37 for a detailed breakdown.

KINGDOM ANIMALIA
Multicellular eukaryotes that develop from a large egg and small sperm through a characteristic series of embryonic stages.
Phylum Poriphera (about 10,000 species)
  Class Calcarea—calcareous sponges
  Class Desmospongiae—sponges with a network of spongin
  Class Sclerospongiae—sponges with a network of spongin and aragonite or silica
Phylum Cnidaria (about 9,400 species)
  Class Hydrozoa—hydras, hydroids, fire corals
  Class Scyphozoa—true jellyfish
  Class Anthozoa—most corals and sea anemones
Phylum Ctenophora (about 90 species)
  Sea gooseberries and comb jellies
Phylum Platyhelminthes (about 15,000 species)
  Class Turbellaria—free-living flatworms
  Class Trematoda—flukes
  Class Cestoda—tapeworms
Phylum Nemertina (about 750 species)
  Ribbonworms
Phylum Rotifera (about 2,000 species)
  Rotifers
Phylum Nematoda (about 80,000 species)
  Nematodes

Phylum Ectoprocta (about 5,000 species)
  Sea mats or moss animals
Phylum Brachiopoda (about 260 species)
  Brachiopods or lamp shells
Phylum Mollusca (about 110,000 species)
  Class Monoplacophora—monoplacophorans
  Class Aplacophora—solenogasters
  Class Polyplacophora—chitons or coat-of-mail shells
  Class Pelecypoda (Bivalvia)—bivalves (clams, mussels, oysters, scallops)
  Class Gastropoda—snails, slugs
  Class Scaphopoda—tooth shells
  Class Cephalopoda—octopus, squid, cuttlefish, nautiluses
Phylum Annelida (about 9,000 species)
  Class Polychaeta—marine bristleworms (lugworm, ragworm)
  Class Oligochaeta—terrestrial bristleworms (earthworms)
  Class Hirudinea—leeches
Phylum Arthropoda (about 1,000,000 species)
  Subphylum Mandibulata (three distinct body parts)
    Class Crustacea—water fleas, shrimps, crabs, copepods, barnacles
    Class Diplopoda—millipedes
    Class Chilopoda—centipedes
    Class Insecta—insects
      Order Thysanura—bristletails, silverfish, firebrats
      Order Isoptera—termites
      Order Dermaptera—earwigs
      Order Collembola—springtails
      Order Ephemeroptera—mayflies
      Order Odonata—dragonflies
      Order Orthoptera—grasshoppers, crickets, mantids
      Order Dictyoptera—cockroaches
      Order Phasmida—stick insects, leaf insects
      Order Hemiptera—true bugs
      Order Homoptera—cicadas, aphids
      Order Lepidoptera—butterflies, moths
      Order Diptera—flies
      Order Siphonaptera—fleas
      Order Mallophaga—chewing lice
      Order Hymenoptera—wasps, bees, ants, hornets
      Order Coleoptera—beetles
      Order Trichoptera—caddis flies
  Subphylum Chelicerata (two distinct body parts)
    Class Pycnogonida—sea spiders
    Class Merostomata—horseshoe crabs or king crabs
    Class Arachnida—spiders, scorpions, harvestmen, mites, ticks
Phylum Echinodermata (about 600 species)
  Class Crinoidea—sea lilies, feather stars
  Class Holothuroidea—sea cucumbers
  Class Echinoidea—sea urchins, sand dollars
  Class Asteroidea—starfish or sea stars
  Class Ophiurodea—brittlestars

Phylum Chordata (about 45,000 species)
  Subphylum Tunicata (no brain, only larva has notochord
      and nerve cord, adult secretes cellulose tunic)
    Class Larvacea—larvaceans (tadpolelike)
    Class Ascidiacea—sea squirts
    Class Cephalochordata—lancelets
  Subphylum Agnatha—brain and skull, no jaws or paired
      appendages
    Class Cyclostomata—no scales, round suckerlike mouth
      Order Myxiniformes—hagfish
      Order Petromyzontiformes—lampreys
  Subphylum Gnathostomata (brain and skull, jaws and
      paired appendages)
    Superclass Pisces (jawed fish)
      Class Chondrichthyes—cartilaginous fish (about
          700 species)
        Order Chlamydoselachiformes—frill sharks
        Order Hexanchiformes—cow sharks
        Order Heterodontiformes—bullhead sharks
        Order Squaliformes—most other sharks
        Order Rajiiformes—rays, sawfish, guitarfish, skates
        Order Chimaeriformes—chimaeras
      Class Osteichthyes—bony fish (about 21,000 species)
        Order Coelacanthiformes—coelacanths
        Order Dipteriformes—lungfish
        Order Polypteriformes—bichirs
        Order Acipenseriformes—sturgeons, paddlefish
        Order Semionotiformes—gars
        Order Amiiformes—bowfins
        Order Elopiformes—tarpons, bonefish
        Order Anguilliformes—eels, morays, gulpers
        Order Clupeiformes—herrings, anchovies
        Order Osteoglossiformes—arapaimas, freshwater
            butterflyfish, mooneyes, featherbacks
        Order Salmoniformes—salmon, trout, grayling,
            whitefish, pike
        Order Myctophiformes—lizardfish, lanternfish
        Order Gonorynchiformes—milkfish
        Order Cypriniformes—hatchetfish, electric eels,
            minnows, carp, suckers, loaches
        Order Siluriformes—catfish
        Order Gadiformes—cod, pearlfish, eelpout,
            grenadiers
        Order Atheriniformes—flying fish, foureye fish,
            silversides
        Order Zeiformes—dories
        Order Lampridiformes—opahs, ribbonfish, oarfish
        Order Gasterosteiformes—sticklebacks, trumpet
            fish, seahorses
        Order Scorpaeniformes—scorpionfish, rockfish,
            lumpfish
        Order Perciformes—sea bass, tuna, perch, snappers,
            archerfish, barracudas, parrotfish, mackerel,
            swordfish
        Order Pleuronectiformes—flounders, soles, plaice
        Order Tetraodontiformes—triggerfish, puffers
    Superclass Tetrapoda (four-legged vertebrates)
      Class Amphibia—amphibians (about 2,400 species)
        Order Urodela—salamanders, mud puppies, newts
        Order Anura—frogs, toads
        Order Apoda—caecilians
      Class Reptilia—reptiles (about 6,600 species)
        Order Chelonia—turtles, tortoises
        Order Squamata—lizards, snakes, geckos, iguanas
        Order Crocodylia—crocodiles, alligators, caimans
      Class Aves (about 9,300 species)
        Order Struthioniformes—ostrich
        Order Rheiformes—rheas

Order Casuariiformes—emus, cassowaries
Order Apterygiformes—kiwis
Order Tinamiformes—tinamous
Order Sphenisciformes—penguins
Order Gaviformes—loons or divers
Order Podicipediformes—grebes, dabchicks
Order Procellariiformes—albatrosses, shearwaters,
    petrels
Order Pelecaniformes—pelicans, gannets, boobies,
    cormorants
Order Ciconiiformes—herons, storks, ibises,
    spoonbills, flamingoes
Order Anseriforms—screamers, ducks, geese,
    swans
Order Falconiformes—vultures and diurnal birds of
    prey
Order Galliformes—grouse, pheasants, turkeys, quail
Order Gruiformes—cranes, rails, coots, bustards
Order Charadriiformes—plovers, gulls, terns, auks,
    waders
Order Pteroclidiformes—sandgrouse
Order Columbiformes—pigeons, doves
Order Psittaciformes—parrots, lories, cockatoos,
    macaws
Order Cuculiformes—cuckoos, roadrunners
Order Strigiformes—owls
Order Caprimulgiformes—nightjars, frogmouths,
    oilbirds
Order Apodiformes—swifts, hummingbirds
Order Coliiformes—mousebirds
Order Trogoniformes—trogons
Order Coraciiformes—kingfishers, bee-eaters,
    hornbills
Order Piciformes—woodpeckers, sapsuckers,
    honeyguides, toucans
Order Passeriformes—perching birds
  Class Mammalia (about 4,000 species)
    Subclass Protheria—egg-laying mammals or
        monotremes
      Order Monotremata—echidnas or spiny anteaters,
          duck-billed platypus
    Subclass Theria—all other mammals
      Infraclass Metatheria—marsupials or pouched
          mammals
      Infraclass Eutheria—placental mammals
        Order Insectivora—hedgehogs, moles, shrews
        Order Dermoptera—flying lemurs
        Order Chiroptera—bats, flying foxes
        Order Primates—tree shrews, lemurs,
            monkeys, apes, humans
        Order Edentata—sloths, anteaters, armadillos
        Order Pholidota—pangolins or scaly anteaters
        Order Lagomorpha—rabbits, hares, pikas
        Order Rodentia—rats, mice, beavers,
            squirrels, porcupines
        Order Cetacea—whales, dolphins, porpoises
        Order Carnivora—dogs, bears, raccoons,
            weasels, hyenas, cats
        Order Pinnipedia—seals, sea lions, walruses
        Order Tubulidentata—aardvark or ant bear
        Order Proboscidea—elephants
        Order Hyracoidea—hyraxes
        Order Sineria—manatees, dugongs, sea cows
        Order Perissodactyla (odd-toed ungulates)—
            horses, zebras, tapirs, rhinoceroses
        Order Artiodactyla (even-toed ungulates)—
            pigs, camels, deer, cattle, goats, antelopes,
            sheep

Classification of Plants

The plant kingdom can be divided in various ways. One major split is into nonvascular and vascular plants. Nonvascular plants are the bryophytes (such as mosses and liverworts). They have no phloem or xylem tissue to carry water and nutrients around the plant. Vascular plants, which do contain these tissues, are all the others. Two major groups among the vascular plants are the gymnosperms—cone-bearing plants such as conifers and cycads—and angiosperms—the flowering plants. Not all botanists agree on details of plant classification, but the following scheme is generally accepted.

NONVASCULAR PLANTS

Division Bryophyta

These plants have no true leaves, stems, or roots, and reproduce by means of spores. Most live in damp places and need water in order to reproduce.

Class Anthocerotae

Hornworts make up this class. They are small plants, up to 0.75 in. [2 cm] across, with a ribbonlike gametophyte. Cylindrical sporangia—resembling horns—growing continuously from the base of the plant contain the spores.

Class Hepaticae

This class consists of the liverworts. The low-growing gametophyte may be leafy or flat and ribbonlike. There are up to 9,000 different species of liverworts.

Class Musci

This class contains the true mosses. The gametophyte is leafy with horizontal or upright stems that give rise to spore-carrying sporangia. There are up to 14,000 species. A well-known genus is *Sphagnum*.

VASCULAR PLANTS

Division Psilophyta

This division includes the rare plants known as fork ferns or whisk ferns. They grow in warm parts of the world and have thin, branched stems but no roots. The gametophytes grow underground.

Division Lycophyta

This division includes club mosses, quillworts, and spike mosses. They generally grow on damp forest floors and have roots, stems, and leaves, with spore-containing sporangia on the stems or leaves. There are more than 1,200 species. A typical genus is *Selaginella*.

Division Sphenophyta

Horsetails make up this division. They have tiny leaves growing around the jointed stems, which grow up to 3 ft. [90 cm] long. There is only one genus, *Psilotum*.

Division Pterophyta

The pterophytes are the ferns. They reproduce by spores that form beneath the fronds (leaves). They vary greatly in size from microscopic plants to tree ferns more than 70 ft. [21.3 m] tall. There are more than 12,000 species. The divisions Lycophyta, Sphenophyta, and Pterophyta together make up the group known as pteridophytes.

Division Ginkgophyta

The ginkgo is a tree with fan-shaped leaves that grow from its many branches, which also bear the foul-smelling fleshy seeds at their ends. There is only one species, *Ginkgo bilboa*.

Division Cycadophyta

Cycads have fernlike or palmlike leaves that, in some species, grow directly from a single underground stem. They bear large seed cones, with male and female cones on different plants. There are about 100 species.

Division Coniferophyta

Most conifers are evergreen shrubs or trees with needle-shaped or scalelike leaves. They bear their seeds in cones. There are about 400 species arranged in about fifty genera, including *Abies* (firs), *Cupressus* (cypresses), *Pinus* (pines), *Sequoia*, and *Taxodiu* (yews).

Division Gnetophyta

The gnetophytes are a small, unusual group of widely varying plants that grow in tropical regions. The reproductive structure resembles a flower, although it is not a true flower. The three genera include *Welwitschia*, an African desert plant that has two large woody leaves that lie on the ground.

Division Anthophyta

This division consists of the angiosperms, or flowering plants. The sex cells are in the flowers, with the female ova fertilized by the male pollen. The seeds are enclosed in a fruit that develops from an ovary. There are more than 250,000 species.

Class Monocotyledonae

Monocotyledons, or monocots, have a single seed leaf (cotyledon). The flowers' petals usually occur in multiples of three, and the leaves have main veins that run parallel to each other. There are 40,000 or so species, which include grasses, irises, lilies, palms, and orchids.

Class Dicotyledonae

Dicotyledons, or dicots, have two seed leaves. Petals usually occur in multiples of four or five, and the leaves have a complex network of veins. There are about 210,000 species.

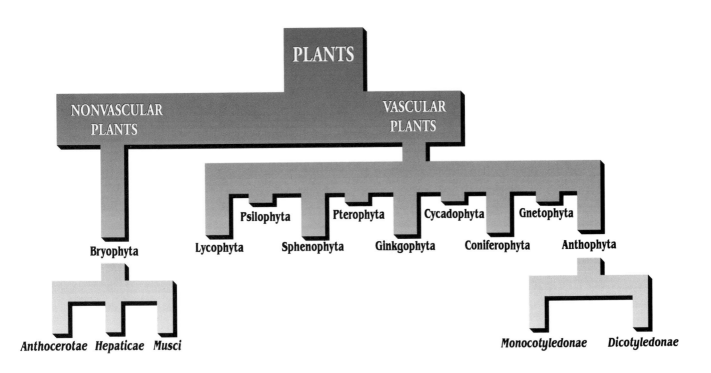

Endangered Species

Every day, several species of plants and animals become extinct, nearly always because of the activities of humans. Animals may become extinct because they are overhunted or because their habitats are destroyed. Pesticides and pollution also increase the numbers of endangered species. Attempts to reverse the trend include growing rare plants in botanical gardens, and breeding rare animals in zoos and then releasing them into the wild.

ENDANGERED PLANTS

Common name	Location
African violet	Tanzania
Arizona agave	Arizona (USA)
Augusta kennedia	Southwest Australia
Bandera County ancistrocactus	Texas (USA)
Big-leaf palm	Madagascar
Bois de fer	Seychelles
Bois de prune blanc	Mauritius
Cacao de monte	Ecuador
Caiapia	Brazil
Caoba	Ecuador
Chatham Island's forget-me-not	Chatham Island (New Zealand)
Costa Rican jatropha	Costa Rica
Cycads—14 species of the order are endangered	
Dalla	Egypt, Sudan
Dirachma	Socotra (South Yemen)
Drury's slipper orchid	India
Flor de mayo	Canary Islands
Golden gladiolus	Southern Africa
Grantham's camilla	Hong Kong
Hamilton's gunnera	Stewart Island (New Zealand)
Hayun lago	Guam, Western Pacific
Hooded helleborine orchid	Crete (Greece)
Horseshoe fern	Lord Howe Island (Australia)
Jasmine-flowered heath	Southern Africa
Kauai hesperomannia	Hawaii (USA)
Kauai silversword	Hawaii (USA)
Knowlton cactus	New Mexico (USA)
Lobster claw	New Zealand
Louisiana quillwort	Louisiana (USA)
Mauritian crinum lily	Mauritius
Michay rojo	Chile
Mogumber bell	Australia
Neogomesia cactus	Mexico
North American pawpaw	Florida (USA)
Old father live forever	St. Helena
Palma corcho	Cuba
Palms—91 species of the family are endangered	
Pininiana	Canary Islands (Spain)
Saiberbher	Socotra (South Yemen)
St. Helena redwood	St. Helena
Sicilian fir	Sicily
Snow mimosa	Brazil
Socotran pomegranate	Socotra (South Yemen)
Tarout cypress	Algeria
Tennessee green pitcher plant	Tennessee (USA)
Underground orchid	Southwest Australia
Virginia round-leaf birch	Virginia (USA)
Wallich's elm	Afghanistan, India, Nepal, Pakistan
White gum	Australia
Yeheb nut	Ethiopia

ENDANGERED MAMMALS

Common name	Location
Addax	Sahara, Sahel
African wild ass	Northwest Africa
Amami rabbit	Japan
Amargosa vole	California (USA)
Arabian oryx	Middle East
Arabian tahr	Oman, United Arab Emirates
Asian elephant	Asia
Aye-aye	Madagascar
Baluchistan bear	Iran, Pakistan, Cameroon
Barbados raccoon	Barbados
Black colobus	Western Africa
Black-footed ferret	USA
Black rhinoceros	Eastern and southern Africa
Blue whale	Arctic, Atlantic, Pacific oceans
Bowhead whale	Arctic, Atlantic, Pacific oceans
Brindled nailtail wallaby	Queensland (Australia)
Broad-nosed gentle lemur	Madagascar
Brush-tailed bettong	Australia
Buffy-headed marmoset	Brazil
Buffy-tufted-ear marmoset	Brazil
Cabrera's hutia	Cuba
Caribbean monk seal	Caribbean
Central American squirrel monkey	Costa Rica
Chapman's fruit bat*	Philippines
Colorado River cotton rat	California (USA)
Comoros black flying fox	Comoros
Cotton-top tamarin	Colombia
Cuban solenodon	Cuba
Cuvier's gazelle	Northwest Africa
Drill	Western Africa
Dwarf hutia	Cuba
Fea's muntjac	Burma, Thailand
Florida cougar	Florida (USA)
Fox squirrel delmarva	Maryland (USA)
Fresno kangaroo rat	California (USA)
Ghizhou snub-nosed monkey	Vietnam, Laos
Giant golden mole	Southern Africa
Golden-headed lion tamarin	Brazil
Golden lion tamarin	Brazil
Golden-rumped lion tamarin	Brazil
Gray bat	Southeast Asia
Great Indian rhinoceros	India, Nepal
Greater bilby	Northern Australia
Grevy's zebra	Ethiopia, Kenya
Hairy-eared dwarf lemur	Madagascar
Haitian solenodon	Hispaniola (Haiti)
Hawaiian monk seal	Hawaii (USA)

Denotes species that may already be extinct

Common name	Location
Hispid hare	Himalayas
Humpback whale	Most oceans
Indris	Madagascar
Indus River dolphin	Pakistan
Iriomote cat	Japan
Japanese sea lion	Japan, Korea
Javan gibbon	Java (Indonesia)
Javan leaf monkey	Java (Indonesia)
Javan rhinoceros	Java (Indonesia)
Jentink's duiker	Ivory Coast, Liberia
Kirk's colobus	Zanzibar (Tanzania)
Kloss's gibbon	Mentawai Island (Indonesia)
Kouprey	Indochina
Large-eared hutia	Cuba
Liberian mongoose	Liberia, Ivory Coast
Lion-tailed macaque	Southern India
Little earth hutia	Cuba
Lowland anoa	Sulawesi (Indonesia)
Malayan tapir	Southeast Asia
Maned sloth	Brazil
Mediterranean monk seal	Mediterranean
Mentawai leaf monkey	Mentawai Island (Indonesia)
Mentawai macaque	Mantawai Island (Indonesia)
Mountain anoa	Sulawesi (Indonesia)
Mountain nyala	Ethiopia
Nilgiri leaf monkey	Southern India
Northern hairy-nosed wombat	Australia
Northern right whale	North Atlantic, North Pacific
Numbat	Australia
Orangutan	Borneo, Sumatra
Pakistan sand cat	Pakistan
Pardel lynx	Portugal
Persian fallow deer	Iraq
Philippine tarsier	Philippines
Philippines tube-nosed fruit bat	Philippines
Pig-tailed langur	Mentawai Island (Indonesia)
Prueuss's guenon	Nigeria, Benin
Przewalski's horse*	China, Mongolia
Puerto Rican flower bat*	Puerto Rico
Pygmy hog	India, Nepal
Red colobus	Eastern, central, western Africa
Red wolf	Texas, Louisiana (USA)

Common name	Location
Red-shanked douc monkey	Vietnam, Laos
Riverine rabbit	Southern Africa
Rodrigues flying fox	Mauritius
Russet-eared guenon	Nigeria
Saimaa seal	Finland
Samoan flying fox	Samoa
San Quentin kangaroo rat	Baja California (Mexico)
Scimitar-horned oryx	Sahara, Sahel
Seychelles sheath-tailed bat	Seychelles
Shansi sika	Japan
Simien fox	Ethiopia
Snow leopard	Asia
South Andean huemul	Andes
Sumatran rhinoceros	Southeast Asia
Sumatran serow	Sumatra
Swamp deer	India, Nepal
Tamaraw	Philippines
Tana River mangabey	Kenya
Tanzanian woolly bat*	Tanzania
Tehuantepec hare	Mexico
Tiger	Asia
Tonkin leaf monkey	Indochina, southwest China
Tonkin snub-nosed monkey	Vietnam
Vancouver Island marmot	Canada
Visayan spotted deer	Philippines
Volcano rabbit	Mexico
Walia ibex	Ethiopia
West African chimpanzee	Western Africa
White rhinoceros	Eastern and southern Africa
White throated guenon	Nigeria, Benin
White-headed black leaf monkey	Southern China
Wild Asiatic water buffalo	India, Nepal
Wild yak	Central Asia
Woodlark Island cuscus	Papua New Guinea
Woolly spider monkey	Brazil
Yangtze River dolphin	China
Yellow-tailed woolly monkey	Ecuador, Peru
Yunnan snub-nosed monkey	China
Zanzibar suni	Zanzibar (Tanzania)

* Denotes species that may already be extinct

Minerals and Human Diet

The human body needs small amounts of minerals in order to stay healthy. We take in these minerals with our food, and a balanced diet contains all the minerals we need. But if the diet does not contain enough of a particular mineral, a deficiency disease may result. This table lists functions and sources of various minerals.

MINERAL	FUNCTION IN THE BODY	SOURCES IN HUMAN DIET	DEFICIENCY DISEASES
Calcium Ca^{2+}	Component of bones and teeth. Also needed for blood clotting, nerve action, and muscle contraction. Enzyme activator.	Milk, cheese, fish, hard drinking water, eggs, leafy green vegetables	Poor skeletal growth, soft bones, muscular spasms, slow blood clotting
Chlorine Cl^-	Needed to maintain the balance between cations and anions, and for the activity of excitable tissue, notably muscle and nerve receptors. Formation of hydrochloric acid. Needed for carbon dioxide transport in the blood.	Most foods, including table salt	Muscular cramps
Cobalt Co^{2+}	Trace mineral that is a constituent of vitamin B_{12}. Needed for the formation of red blood cells.	Liver, red meat, eggs	Pernicious anemia
Copper Cu^{2+}	Trace mineral needed in the formation of hemoglobin and bone. It is found in many enzymes and in the blood.	Most foods, including liver, fish, wheat, beans	Anemia
Fluorine F^-	Trace mineral found in bones and teeth. Improves resistance to dental cavities.	Fluoridated drinking water	Tooth decay and generally weak teeth, especially in the young
Iodine I^-	Component of the growth hormone thyroxine, which controls metabolic rate.	Seafood, iodized table salt, cereals	Goiter (abnormal enlargement of thyroid gland); cretinism in children
Iron Fe^{2+}	Metallic ion required for many enzymes and electron carriers. A key component of hemoglobin and myoglobin in the blood, and contributor to other blood pigments.	Meat, liver, eggs	Anemia
Magnesium Mg^{2+}	Component of bones and teeth. Enzyme activator.	Most foods, especially meat, whole grains, green vegetables	Irritability, convulsions, depression
Manganese Mn^{2+}	Activates various enzymes and contributes to the growth of bones.	Most foods, including liver	Malformation of the skeleton
Molybdenum Mo^{4+}	Required by various enzymes involved in uric acid production.	Liver, green vegetables	
Phosphorous PO_4^{3-}	Constituent of phospholipids in membranes, nucleotides (such as ATP), and nucleic acids. Also found in bones and teeth. Needed for nerve and muscle action.	Most foods	
Potassium K^+	Determines the cation-anion balance in intracellular fluid and is required for the action of excitable tissue, such as nerve and muscle cells. Cofactor in respiration.	Meat, fruits and vegetables	Muscular weakness
Sodium Na^+	Needed for nerve and muscle action and helps determine osmotic pressure and the anion-cation balance.	Most foods, including table salt	Muscular cramps; overconsumption may result in high blood pressure
Sulfate SO_4^{2-}	Component of proteins and coenzymes.	Meat, dairy foods, eggs	
Zinc Zn^{2+}	Required to activate about 70 different enzymes, and involved in insulin metabolism and in carbon dioxide transport in the blood.	Most foods, especially liver, meat, fish	

Vitamins and Human Diet

Small amounts of vitamins are needed in the diet for good health. A balanced diet contains all the vitamins we need. Lack of a particular vitamin may lead to a deficiency disease. For example, lack of niacin (vitamin B_3) causes pellagra. This table lists the functions and sources of the vitamins needed by human beings.

VITAMIN	FUNCTION IN THE BODY	SOURCES IN HUMAN DIET	DEFICIENCY DISEASES
A Retinol	Needed for the formation of the visual pigment in the eye. Promotes skin growth.	Fish-liver oil, liver, milk, broccoli, cabbage, carrots, apricots	Poor night vision; dry skin; dry mucous membranes; blindness
B_1 Thiamine	Involved in cellular respiration and break down of carbohydrate, converting pyruvic acid to acetyl coenzyme A.	Liver, nuts, potatoes, yeast, eggs, whole grains	Beriberi, neuritis, heart failure, slows children's growth
B_2 Riboflavin	Coenzyme in protein and carbohydrate metabolism. Vital constituent of electron carriers.	Leafy green vegetables, fish, eggs, milk, yeast, cheese, liver	Sore mouth, ulcerations, eye irritation
B_3 Niacin	Coenzymes (NAD and NADP) required as hydrogen acceptors in the functioning of cells.	Meat, yeast, liver, whole-grain bread	Pellagra, skin lesions, rashes, fatigue, diarrhea
B_5 Pantothenic acid	Forms acetyl coenzyme A, which activates carboxylic acids in the functioning of cells.	Most foods, especially yeast, eggs	Fatigue, poor coordination, muscle cramps
B_6 Pyridoxine	Part of coenzyme A involved in biochemical reactions of amino acids and fatty acids.	Most foods, especially yeast, whole grains, fish, liver, legumes	Anemia, convulsions, dermatitis, nervous disorders, diarrhea
B_{12} Cyanocobalamin	Coenzyme required for ribonucleic acid (RNA) synthesis. Also required in the liver for red blood cell formation.	Meat, eggs, fish, dairy foods	Pernicious anemia, malformation of red blood cells
Biotin	Coenzyme in carboxylation reactions. Involved in protein synthesis.	Most foods	Dermatitis and muscle pains
Folic acid	Required for nucleic protein synthesis and the formation of red blood cells.	Leafy green vegetables, liver, yeast, fruits	Pernicious anemia
C Ascorbic acid	Involved in the formation of connective tissues; intercellular cement for bone and cartilage; maintains resistance to infection; frees iron to make hemoglobin.	Citrus fruits, green vegetables, tomatoes, potatoes	Scurvy, anemia, slow wound healing, heart failure
D Calciferol	Controls absorption and reactions of calcium and phosphorous, and involved in the formation and hardening of bones and teeth.	Fish-liver oil, dairy foods, eggs, liver, yeast, sunlight on skin	Rickets, osteomalacia
E Tocopherol	Not well understood. Protects red blood cells and is important in muscle maintenance.	Green vegetables, vegetable oils, eggs, wheat germ	Bursting of red blood cells, sterility, nervous defects, muscular dystrophy
K Phylloquinone	Required in the liver for synthesis of prothrombin.	Leafy green vegetables, pork, liver	Prolonged clotting time, especially in newborns

World National Parks

Many countries have established national parks to preserve various species of wildlife and their habitats. The world's first—Yellowstone National Park in Wyoming—dates from 1872. Today, there are more than five thousand sites on the United Nations List of National Parks and Protected Areas, ranging in size from the Northeast Greenland National Park (173 million acres [70 million hectares]) to small islands of only a few hundred acres. This table lists world national parks with an area of more than 170,000 acres [69,000 hectares].

LOCATION	AREA (ACRES)	(HECTARES)
Africa		
Banc d'Arguin, Mauritania	2,898,500	1,173,000
Benoue, Cameroon	444,800	180,000
Bikuar, Angola	1,952,100	790,000
Boma, Sudan	5,633,900	2,280,000
Bouche du Baoule, Mali	864,800	350,000
Chobe, Botswana	2,466,100	998,000
Dinder, Sudan	2,199,200	890,000
El Kala, Algeria	189,000	76,500
Etosha, Namibia	5,503,000	2,227,000
Fazao-Malfakassa, Togo	474,400	192,000
Gile, Mozambique	518,900	210,000
Hwange (Wankie), Zimbabwe	3,620,000	1,465,000
Iona, Angola	3,743,600	1,515,000
Isalo, Madagascar	201,400	81,500
Kahuzi-Beiga, Zaire	1,482,600	600,000
Kainji Lake, Nigeria	1,322,000	535,000
Kalahari Gemsbok, South Africa	2,369,700	959,000
Kasungu, Malawi	592,000	231,500
Kisama, Angola	2,461,100	996,000
Korup, Cameroon	311,300	126,000
Kruger, South Africa	4,942,000	2,000,000
Mana Pools, Zimbabwe	542,400	219,500
Masa, Morocco	178,000	72,000
Monovo-Gounda-St. Floris, Central African Republic	4,299,500	1,740,000
Moremi, Botswana	963,700	390,000
Namib-Naukluft, Namibia	12,298,200	4,977,000
Niokolo-Koba, Senegal	2,256,000	913,000
Po, Burkina	384,200	155,500
South Luangwa, Zambia	2,236,300	905,000
Tasssili N'Ajjer, Algeria	741,300	300,000
Tsavo, Kenya	5,144,600	2,082,000
Virunga, Zaire	1,927,400	780,000
Zakouma, Chad	741,300	300,000
Zinave, Mozambique	1,235,500	500,000
Asia		
Akan, Japan	223,600	90,500
Alaungdaw Kathapa, Burma	396,600	160,500
Asir, Saudi Arabia	1,025,500	415,000
Aso, Japan	179,100	72,500
Bandai-Asahi, Japan	468,300	189,500
Bandipur, India	216,200	87,500
Beydaglari, Turkey	174,200	70,500
Daisetsuzan, Japan	570,800	231,000
Fuji-Hakone-Izu, Japan	302,700	122,500
Golestan, Iran	227,300	92,000
Kanha, Bangladesh	232,300	94,000
Khao Yai, Thailand	536,200	217,000
Khunjerab, Jammu and Kashmir	560,900	227,000
Kirthar, Pakistan	763,500	309,00
Komodo, Indonesia	185,300	75,000
Mount Apo, Philippines	180,400	73,000
Mount Kinabalu, Brunei	186,600	75,500
Namdapha, India	490,500	198,500
Royal Bardia, India/Nepal	239,700	97,000
Royal Chitwan, Nepal	229,800	93,000
Ruhana, Sri Lanka	242,200	98,000
Sagarmartha, Nepal	284,200	115,000
Sundarbans, India	328,600	133,000
Taman Negara, Malaysia	1,073,600	434,500
Tanjung Puting, Indonesia	877,200	355,000
Ujung Kulon, Indonesia	194,000	78,500
Uromiyeh, Iran	3,201,200	1,295,500
Wilpattu, Sri Lanka	326,200	132,000
Australia and New Zealand		
Arthur's Pass, New Zealand	233,500	94,500
Fiordland, New Zealand	3,093,700	1,252,000
Flinders Ranges, Australia	198,900	80,500
Great Barrier Reef, Australia	49,420,000	20,000,000
Kakadu, Australia	1,648,200	667,000
Mount Aspiring, New Zealand	705,500	285,500
Nelson Lakes, New Zealand	237,216	96,000
Simpson Desert, Australia	1,711,200	692,500
Tongariro, New Zealand	189,000	76,500
Uluru (Ayers Rock), Australia	327,400	132,500
Urewera, New Zealand	512,700	207,500
Western Tasmania Wilderness, Australia	189,000	76,500
Westland/Mount Cook, New Zealand	463,300	187,500
Wet Tropics of Queensland, Australia	2,273,300	920,000

LOCATION	AREA (ACRES)	(HECTARES)
Europe and Russia		
Borgefjell, Norway	268,100	108,500
Brecon Beacons, Great Britain	332,300	134,500
Cévennes, France	798,100	323,000
Dartmoor, Great Britain	236,000	95,500
Doñana, Spain	186,600	75,500
Ecrins, France	266,900	108,000
Gennargentu, Italy	247,100	100,000
German–Luxembourg, Luxembourg	179,100	72,500
Gran Paradiso, Italy	180,400	73,000
Hardangervidda, Norway	847,600	343,000
Hohe Tauem, Austria	617,800	250,000
Lake District, Great Britain	563,400	228,000
Lake Sevan, Russia	370,700	150,000
Lemmenjoki, Finland	691,900	280,000
Neidere Tauern, Austria	185,300	75,000
Nordfriesisches Wattenmeer, Germany	704,200	285,000
North York Moors, Great Britain	341,000	138,000
Ovre Anarjakka, Norway	343,500	139,000
Ovre Dividial, Norway	182,900	74,000
Padjelanta, Sweden	490,500	198,500
Peak District, Great Britain	350,900	142,000
Sarek, Sweden	486,800	197,000
Snowdonia, Great Britain	541,100	219,000
Stelvio, Italy	338,500	137,000
Stora Sjofallet, Sweden	316,300	128,000
Sumava, Czechoslovakia	412,700	167,000
Tatransky, Czechoslovakia	190,300	77,000
Urho Kekkonen, Finland	625,200	253,000
Yorkshire Dales, Great Britain	434,900	176,000
North America		
Armando Bermudez, Dominican Republic	189,000	76,500
Badlands, United States	481,800	195,000
Banff, Canada	1,640,700	664,000
Big Bend, United States	699,300	283,000
Darién , Panama	1,475,200	597,000
Everglades, United States	1,398,600	566,000
Glacier, United States	1,013,100	410,000
Grand Canyon, United States	672,100	272,000
Grand Teton, United States	306,400	124,000
Great Smoky Mountains, United States	518,900	210,000
Gros Morne, Canada	479,400	194,000

LOCATION	AREA (ACRES)	(HECTARES)
Guanacaste, Costa Rica	174,200	70,500
Hawaii Volcanoes, United States	229,800	93,000
Inagua, Bahamas	184,100	74,500
Isle Royale, United States	532,500	215,500
Jasper, Canada	2,688,400	1,088,000
Katmai, United States	4,092,000	1,656,000
Kluane, Canada	5,440,000	2,201,500
Kootenay, Canada	341,000	138,000
Mount Rainier, United States	240,900	97,500
Nahanni, Canada	1,177,400	476,500
Northeast Greenland, Denmark	172,970,000	70,000,000
Northern Ellesmere Island, Canada	9,760,500	3,950,000
Northern Yukon, Canada	2,513,000	1,017,000
Olympic, United States	897,000	363,000
Pacific Rim, Canada	363,200	147,000
Polar Bear Pass, Canada	200,200	81,000
Riding Mountain, Canada	735,100	297,500
Rocky Mountains, United States	263,200	106,500
Sequoia, United States	402,800	163,000
Sierra Maestra, Cuba	1,235,500	500,000
Wrangell-St. Elias, United States	13,193,900	5,339,500
Yellowstone, United States	2,220,200	898,500
Yoho, Canada	323,700	131,000
Yosemite, United States	761,100	308,000
South America		
Amazonia, Brazil	2,471,000	1,000,000
Banados del Este, Brazil	494,200	200,000
Canaima, Venezuela	7,413,000	3,000,000
Chiribiquete, Colombia	2,471,000	1,000,000
Defensores del Chaco, Paraguay	1,927,400	780,000
Galapágos, Ecuador	1,707,500	691,000
Iguaçu, Argentina	2,718,100	1,100,000
Isiboro Sécure, Bolivia	2,471,000	1,000,000
La Neblina, Venezuela	3,360,600	1,360,000
Los Alerces, Argentina	649,900	263,000
Los Glaciares, Argentina	1,102,100	446,000
Manu, Peru	3,788,000	1,533,000
Nahuel Huapi, Argentina	1,057,600	428,000
Sierra Nevada de Santa Marta, Colombia	946,400	383,000
Vincente Pérez Rosales, Chile	543,600	220,000

Wind-chill Factor

Estimated wind speed (in m.p.h)	Actual Thermometer Reading (°F)											
	50	40	30	20	10	0	-10	-20	-30	-40	-50	-60
	Equivalent Temperature (°F)											
Calm	50	40	30	20	10	0	-10	-20	-30	-40	-50	-60
5	48	37	27	16	6	-5	-15	-26	-36	-47	-57	-68
10	40	28	16	4	-9	-24	-33	-46	-58	-70	-83	-95
15	36	22	9	-5	-18	-32	-45	-58	-72	-85	-99	-112
20	32	18	4	-10	-25	-39	-53	-67	-82	-96	-110	-124
25	30	16	0	-15	-29	-44	-59	-74	-88	-104	-118	-133
30	28	13	-2	-18	-33	-48	-63	-79	-94	-109	-125	-140
35	27	11	-4	-20	-35	-51	-67	-82	-98	-113	-129	-145
40	26	10	-6	-21	-37	-53	-69	-85	-100	-116	-132	-148
(Wind speeds greater than 40 m.p.h. have little additional effect.)	Little danger (for properly clothed person)				Increasing danger (danger from freezing of exposed flesh)				Great danger			

Numerals

Various number systems have been used at various times. Roman numerals are still sometimes seen on a clockface. There is no zero, and the first ten numerals are shown below. Other Roman numerals include L = 50, C = 100, D = 500, and M = 1,000. The numbers used every day and in most of science are decimal numerals, which have the base 10. Numerals commonly used in computers are binary numbers, which have the base 2. As a result, there are only two digits, 0 and 1, which can be represented in a computer circuit as "off" and "on" pulses of electric current.

Roman	Decimal	Binary
	0	0000
I	1	0001
II	2	00010
III	3	00011
IV	4	00100
V	5	00101
VI	6	00110
VII	7	00111
VIII	8	01000
IX	9	01001
X	10	01010

Mathematical Formulas

In the formulas below, for the areas and volumes of various geometric figures, s = the length of a side, r = the radius, and π (pi) = 3.1416.

Areas		Volumes	
Square	s^2	Cube	s^3
Rectangle	length x width	Rectangular container (cuboid)	
Parallelogram	base x height		length x width x height
Triangle	$\frac{1}{2}$ base x height	Pyramid	$\frac{1}{3}$ length x width x height
Circle	πr^2		
Sphere	$4\pi r^2$	Sphere	$\frac{4}{3}\pi r^3$
		Cone	$\frac{1}{3}\pi r^2$ x height
		Cylinder	πr^2 x height

Fractions

There are various ways of expressing numbers less than 1. Decimal fractions are the most convenient because they can be manipulated just like any other numbers, while fractions such as $\frac{1}{2}$ and $\frac{2}{3}$ are awkward to add, subtract, multiply, and divide. Percentages are common in commerce and business. They are really fractions expressed in hundredths (for example, $6\% = \frac{6}{100}$ and $75\% = \frac{75}{100}$) with the denominator (100) omitted.

Decimal	Fraction	Percentage (%)
0.01	$\frac{1}{100}$	1
0.02	$\frac{1}{50}$	2
0.03	$\frac{3}{100}$	3
0.04	$\frac{1}{25}$	4
0.05	$\frac{1}{20}$	5
0.06	$\frac{3}{50}$	6
0.07	$\frac{7}{100}$	7
0.08	$\frac{2}{25}$	8
0.09	$\frac{9}{100}$	9
0.10	$\frac{1}{10}$	10
0.12	$\frac{3}{25}$	12
0.125	$\frac{1}{8}$	$12\frac{1}{2}$
0.14	$\frac{7}{50}$	14
0.15	$\frac{3}{20}$	15
0.16	$\frac{4}{25}$	16
0.18	$\frac{9}{50}$	18
0.20	$\frac{1}{5}$	20
0.25	$\frac{1}{4}$	25
0.30	$\frac{3}{10}$	30
0.333	$\frac{1}{3}$	$33\frac{1}{3}$
0.40	$\frac{2}{5}$	40
0.50	$\frac{1}{2}$	50
0.60	$\frac{3}{5}$	60
0.666	$\frac{2}{3}$	$66\frac{2}{3}$
0.75	$\frac{3}{4}$	75
0.80	$\frac{4}{5}$	80
0.90	$\frac{9}{10}$	90
1.00	1	100

BIBLIOGRAPHY

ANIMALS

Bailey, Jill. *Gorilla Rescue* (Save Our Species series). Steck-Vaughn Co., 1990. 48p. (gr. 3–4)

—. *Mission Rhino.* Steck-Vaughn Co., 1990. 48p. (gr. 3–4)

—. *Operation Elephant.* Steck-Vaughn Co., 1991. 48p. (gr. 3–4)

—. *Operation Turtle.* Steck-Vaughn Co., 1992. 48p. (gr. 3–4)

—. *Otter Rescue.* Steck-Vaughn Co., 1992. 48p. (gr. 3–4)

—. *Polar Bear Rescue.* Steck-Vaughn Co., 1991. 48p. (gr. 3–4)

—. *Project Dolphin.* Steck-Vaughn Co., 1992. 48p. (gr. 3–4)

—. *Project Panda.* Steck-Vaughn Co., 1990. 48p. (gr. 3–4)

—. *Project Whale.* Steck-Vaughn Co., 1991. 48p. (gr. 3–4)

—. *Save the Macaws.* Steck-Vaughn Co., 1992. 48p. (gr. 3–4)

—. *Save the Snow Leopard.* Steck-Vaughn Co., 1991. 48p. (gr. 3–4)

—. *Save the Tiger.* Steck-Vaughn Co., 1990. 48p. (gr. 3–4)

Becker, Christine. *Cockroaches, Stinkbugs, and Other Creepy Crawlers.* Lowell House, 1966. (gr. 3–6)

Behrand, Katrin. *Cats.* Barron's, 1990. (gr. 3–5)

Bennett, Paul. *Catching a Meal* (Nature's Secrets series). Thomson Learning, 1994. 32p. (gr. 3–5)

—. *Changing Shape.* Thomson Learning, 1994. 32p. (gr. 3–5)

—. *Communicating.* Thomson Learning, 1996. 32p. (gr. 3–5)

—. *Escaping From Enemies.* Thomson Learning, 1995. 32p. (gr. 3–5)

—. *Hibernation.* Thomson Learning, 1995. 32p. (gr. 3–5)

—. *Keeping Clean.* Thomson Learning, 1995. 32p. (gr. 3–5)

—. *Making a Nest.* Thomson Learning, 1994. 32p. (gr. 3–5)

—. *Migration.* Thomson Learning, 1995. 32p. (gr. 3–5)

—. *Raising a Family.* Thomson Learning, 1996. 32p. (gr. 3–5)

Birds and How They Live. Dorling Kindersley, 1992. 64p. (gr. 3+)

Boring, Mel. *Birds, Nest, and Egg.* Northword, 1996. (gr. 3–6)

Bright, Michael. *Alligators and Crocodiles.* Franklin Watts, 1990. 32p. (gr. 5–8)

Burnie, David and Linda Gamlin. *Questions and Answers About Freshwater Animals* (Questions and Answers About series). Kingfisher Books, 1994. 40p. (gr. 3–5)

Chinery, Michael. *Questions and Answers About Seashore Animals* (Questions and Answers About series). Kingfisher Books, 1994. 40p. (gr. 3–5)

Cleave, Andrew. *Hunters* (Pointers series). Raintree Steck-Vaughn Publishers, 1995. 32p. (gr. 4–5)

Corrigan, Patricia. *Manatees for Kids.* Northword, 1996. (gr. 3–6).

Crisp, Peter. *The Whalers* (Remarkable World series). Thomson Learning, 1996. 48p. (gr. 4+)

DeLaunois, Angela. *Kotik the Baby Seal.* Orca, 1996. (gr. 3–6)

—. *Nanook and Naoya.* Orca, 1996. (gr. 3–6)

Dooris, Ellen. *Meet the Arthropods.* Thames and Hudson, 1996. (gr. 4–9)

Downs, Matthew. *Arctic Foxes.* Simon and Schuster, 1995. (gr. 5+)

Evans, Mark. *Fish.* Dorling Kindersley, 1993. 48p. (gr. 3–7)

Fitzsimons, Cecilia. *Animal Habitats* (Nature's Hidden Worlds series). Raintree Steck-Vaughn Publishers, 1996. 48p. (gr. 4–6)

—. *Animal Lives.* Raintree Steck-Vaughn Publishers, 1996. 48p. (gr. 4–6)

—. *Water Life.* Raintree Steck-Vaughn Publishers, 1996. 48p. (gr. 4–6)

Ganeri, Anita. *Jungle Birds* (Pointers series). Raintree Steck-Vaughn Publishers, 1994. 32p. (gr. 4–5)

—. *Sea Mammals.* Raintree Steck-Vaughn Publishers, 1994. 32p. (gr. 4–5)

—. *Tiger Sharks and Other Dangerous Animals* (Young Observer series). Kingfisher Books, 1995. 40p. (gr. 3–6)

Gerholdt, James E. *Alligators* (Remarkable Reptiles series). Abdo and Daughters, 1994. 24p. (gr. 3–4)

—. *Bees* (Incredible Insects series). Abdo and Daughters, 1996. 24p. (gr. 4–6)

—. *Beetles.* Abdo and Daughters, 1996. 24p. (gr. 4–6)

—. *Bugs.* Abdo and Daughters, 1996. 24p. (gr. 4–6)

—. *Butterflies.* Abdo and Daughters, 1996. 24p. (gr. 4–6)

—. *Dragonflies.* Abdo and Daughters, 1996. 24p. (gr. 4–6)

—. *Frogs* (Amazing Amphibians series). Abdo and Daughters, 1994. 24p. (gr. 3–4)

—. *Grasshoppers* (Incredible Insects series). Abdo and Daughters, 1996. 24p. (gr. 4–6)

—. *Lizards* (Remarkable Reptiles series). Abdo and Daughters, 1994. 24p. (gr. 3–4)

—. *Salamanders* (Amazing Amphibians series). Abdo and Daughters, 1994. 24p. (gr. 3–4)

—. *Snakes* (Remarkable Reptiles series). Abdo and Daughters, 1994. 24p. (gr. 3–4)

—. *Toads* (Amazing Amphibians series). Abdo and Daughters, 1994. 24p. (gr. 3–4)

—. *Tree Frogs.* Abdo and Daughters, 1994. 24p. (gr. 3–4)

—. *Turtles* (Remarkable Reptiles series). Abdo and Daughters, 1994. 24p. (gr. 3–4)

Goodall, Jane. *My Life with the Chimpanzees.* Rev. ed. Pocket/Minstrel, 1996. (gr. 3–6)

Goor, R. and N. *Insect Metamorphosis.* Atheneum. 1990. (gr. 5+)

Hadden, Sue. *Insects.* (Weird and Wonderful series). Thomson Learning, 1993. 32p. (gr. 3–5)

Kallen, Stuart. *Precious Creatures: A to Z* (Eco-Reference series). Abdo and Daughters, 1993. 64p. (gr. 4–6)

The Kingfisher Illustrated Encyclopedia of Animals. Kingfisher Books, 1992. 380p. (gr. 3+)

Kump, Christiane. *Seashells, Crabs and Sea Stars.* Northword, 1996. (gr. 3–6)

Linley, Mike. *Snakes* (Weird and Wonderful series). Thomson Learning, 1993. 32p. (gr. 3–5)

Lundberg, Kathryn. *Bats for Kids.* Northword, 1996. (gr. 3–6)

Matero, Robert. *The Birth of a Humpback Whale.* Simon and Schuster/Atheneum, 1996. (gr. 3–6)

Milkins, Colin S. *Fish* (Weird and Wonderful series). Thomson Learning, 1993. 32p. (gr. 3–5)

Oram, Liz and R. Robin Baker. *Bird Migration* (Migration series). Steck-Vaughn Co., 1992. 48p. (gr. 4–7)

—. *Insect Migration.* Steck-Vaughn Co., 1992. 48p. (gr. 4–7)

—. *Mammal Migration.* Steck-Vaughn Co., 1992. 48p. (gr. 4–7)

—. *Migration in the Sea.* Steck-Vaughn Co., 1992. 48p. (gr. 4–7)

O'Toole, Christopher. *Insects and Spiders.* Facts on File, 1990. 96p. (gr. 4–6)

Owen, Oliver. *Calf to Dolphin* (Lifewatch: The Mystery of Nature series). Abdo and Daughters, 1994. 32p. (gr. 4–6)

—. *Caterpillar to Butterfly.* Abdo and Daughters, 1994. 32p. (gr. 4–6)

—. *Cub to Grizzly Bear.* Abdo and Daughters, 1995. 32p. (gr. 4–6)

—. *Egg to Robin.* Abdo and Daughters, 1994. 32p. (gr. 4–6)

—. *Egg to Snake.* Abdo and Daughters, 1994. 32p. (gr. 4–6)

—. *Pup to Timberwolf.* Abdo and Daughters, 1995. 32p. (gr. 4–6)

—. *Tadpole to Frog.* Abdo and Daughters, 1994. 32p. (gr. 4–6)

Parker, Philip. *Your Wild Neighborhood* (Project Eco-City series). Thomson Learning, 1994.

48p. (gr. 4–6)

—. *Your Living Home.* Thomson Learning, 1994. 48p. (gr. 4–6)

Parker, Steve. *Alarming Animals* (Creepy Creatures series). Raintree Steck-Vaughn Publishers, 1993. 40p. (gr. 3–4)

—. *Awesome Amphibians.* Raintree Steck-Vaughn Publishers, 1994. 40p. (gr. 3–4)

—. *Beastly Bugs.* Raintree Steck-Vaughn Publishers, 1993. 40p. (gr. 3–4)

—. *Cunning Carnivores.* Raintree Steck-Vaughn Publishers, 1994. 40p. (gr. 3–4)

—. *Fearsome Fish.* Raintree Steck-Vaughn Publishers, 1994. 40p. (gr. 3–4)

—. *Giraffes.* Millbrook/Cooper Beech, 1996. (gr. 4–6)

—. *How Do We Know Animals Can Think?* (How Do We Know? series). Raintree Steck-Vaughn Publishers, 1995. 48p. (gr. 5–6)

—. *Revolting Reptiles.* Raintree Steck-Vaughn Publishers, 1994. 40p. (gr. 3–4)

—. *Scary Spiders.* Raintree Steck-Vaughn Publishers, 1994. 40p. (gr. 3–4)

—. *Sharks.* Millbrook/Cooper Beech, 1996. (gr. 4–6)

Penny, Malcolm. *Birds of Prey* (Remarkable World series). Thomson Learning, 1996. 48p. (gr. 4+)

—. *Night Creatures.* Thomson Learning, 1996. 48p. (gr. 4+)

Pirotta, Saviour. *Monsters of the Deep* (Remarkable World series). Thomson Learning, 1996. 48p. (gr. 4+)

Pope, Joyce. *Deadly Venom* (Curious Creatures series). Steck-Vaughn Co., 1992. 48p. (gr. 4+)

—. *Life in the Dark.* Steck-Vaughn Co., 1992. 48p. (gr. 4+)

—. *Living Fossils.* Steck-Vaughn Co., 1992. 48p. (gr. 4+)

—. *Making Contact.* Steck-Vaughn Co., 1992. 48p. (gr. 4+)

—. *Mistaken Identity.* Steck-Vaughn Co., 1992. 48p. (gr. 4+)

—. *On the Move.* Steck-Vaughn Co., 1992. 48p. (gr. 4+)

—. *Strange Nature.* Steck-Vaughn Co., 1992. 48p. (gr. 4+)

—. *Two Lives.* Steck-Vaughn Co., 1992. 48p. (gr. 4+)

Redmond, Ian. *Monkeys and Apes.* Mallard Press, 1990. (gr. 3–5)

Riley, Helen. *Frogs and Toads* (Weird and Wonderful series). Thomson Learning, 1993. 32p. (gr. 3–5)

Rock, Maxine. *Kishina: A True Story of Gorilla Survival.* Peachtree, 1996. (gr. 4+)

Savage, Stephen. *Ears* (Adaptation for Survival series). Thomson Learning, 1996. 32p. (gr. 3–5)

—. *Eyes.* Thomson Learning, 1996. 32p. (gr. 3–5)

—. *Hands and Feet.* Thomson Learning, 1996. 32p. (gr. 3–5)

—. *Mouths.* Thomson Learning, 1996. 32p. (gr. 3–5)

—. *Noses.* Thomson Learning, 1996. 32p. (gr. 3–5)

—. *Skin.* Thomson Learning, 1996. 32p. (gr. 3–5)

Sterry, Paul. *Seabirds* (Pointers series). Raintree Steck-Vaughn Publishers, 1995. 32p. (gr. 4–5)

Stidworthy, John. *Land Predators* (Remarkable World series). Thomson Learning, 1996. 48p. (gr. 4+)

Taylor, David. *The Big and Little Animal Book* (Animal Opposites series). Raintree Steck-Vaughn Publishers, 1996. 32p. (gr. 3–4)

—. *The Fast and Slow Animal Book.* Raintree Steck-Vaughn Publishers, 1996. 32p. (gr. 3–4)

—. *The Heavy and Light Animal Book.* Raintree Steck-Vaughn Publishers, 1996. 32p. (gr. 3–4)

—. *The Long Lived and Short Lived Animal Book.* Raintree Steck-Vaughn Publishers, 1996. 32p. (gr. 3–4)

Watts, Barrie. *Dragonfly.* Silver Burdett, 1991. 25p. (gr. 4–6)

Williams, Brian, et al. *Questions and Answers About Forest Animals* (Questions and Answers About series). Kingfisher Books, 1994. 40p. (gr. 3-5)

—. *Questions and Answers About Polar Animals.* Kingfisher Books, 1994. 40p. (gr. 3–5)

BIOGRAPHY

Billings, Charlene W. *Grace Hopper: Navy Admiral and Computer Pioneer*. Enslow, 1989. 128p. (gr. 5+)

Codye, Corinn. *Luis W. Alvarez* (Raintree Hispanic Stories series). Raintree Steck-Vaughn Publishers, 1993. 32p. (gr. 4–5)

Freedman, Russell. *The Wright Brothers: How They Invented the Airplane*. Holiday House, 1991. 132p. (gr. 5+)

Kent, Z. *The Story of Henry Ford and the Automobile*. Children's Press, 1990. (gr. 3–5)

Larousse Dictionary of Scientists. Larousse, 1994. 608p. (gr. 7+)

Mason, Antony. *Peary and Amundsen: Race to the Poles* (Beyond the Horizons series). Raintree Steck-Vaughn Publishers, 1995. 48p. (gr. 5–6)

Reef, Catherine. *Albert Einstein, Scientist of the Twentieth Century*. Dillon, 1991. 63p. (gr. 6+)

Rogers, Teresa. *George Washington Carver: Nature's Trailblazer*. Twenty-first Century, 1992. 72p. (gr. 7+)

Simmons, Alex. *Ben Carson* (Contemporary Biographies series). Raintree Steck-Vaughn Publishers, 1996. 48p. (gr. 4–6)

Sumption, Christine, and Kathleen Thompson. *Carlos Finlay* (Raintree Hispanic Stories series). Raintree Steck-Vaughn Publishers, 1991. 32p. (gr. 4–5)

Twist, Clint. *Charles Darwin* (Beyond the Horizons series). Raintree Steck-Vaughn Publishers, 1994. 48p. (gr. 5–6)

—. *Gagarin and Armstrong*. Raintree Steck-Vaughn Publishers, 1995. 48p. (gr. 5–6)

DINOSAURS

Benton, Michael. *Deinonychus* (Dinoworld series). Kingfisher Books, 1994. 40p. (gr. 3–5)

—. *Dinosaur and Other Prehistoric Animals Factfinder*. Kingfisher Books, 1992. 256p. (gr. 3–8)

—. *How Do We Know Dinosaurs Existed?* (How Do We Know? series). Raintree Steck-Vaughn Publishers, 1995. 48p. (gr. 5–6)

Dixon, Dougal. *Questions and Answers About Dinosaurs* (Questions and Answers About series). Kingfisher Books, 1995. 40p. (gr. 3–5)

—. *The Search for Dinosaurs* (Digging Up the Past series). Thomson Learning, 1996. 48p. (gr. 4–6).

Fitzsimons, Cecilia. *Creatures of the Past* (Nature's Hidden Worlds series). Raintree Steck-Vaughn Publishers, 1996. 48p. (gr. 4–6)

Lauber, Patricia. *Living with Dinosaurs*. Bradbury, 1991. 48p. (gr. 5+)

Storrs, Glenn W. *Stegosaurus* (Dinoworld series). Kingfisher Books, 1994. 40p. (gr. 3–5)

—. *Tyrannosaurus*. Kingfisher Books, 1994. 40p. (gr. 3–5)

Theodorou, Rod. *When Dinosaurs Ruled the Earth* (Remarkable World series). Thomson Learning, 1996. 48p. (gr. 4+)

Unwin, David. *Brachiosaurus* (Dinoworld series). Kingfisher Books, 1994. 40p. (gr. 3–5

EARTH SCIENCE

Alessandrello, Anna. *The Earth* (Beginnings—Origins and Evolution series). Raintree Steck-Vaughn Publishers, 1995. 48p. (gr. 6–7)

Atkinson, Stuart. *Storms and Hurricanes*. EDC/Usborne, 1996. (gr. 5–10)

Baines, John. *Water* (Resources series). Thomson Learning, 1993. 32p. (gr. 3–6)

Benanti, Carole. *Gemstones*. Random House, 1994. 32p. (gr. 3+)

Bennett, Paul. *Earth: The Incredible Recycling Machine*. Thomson Learning, 1993. 48p. (gr. 3–5)

Benson, Marjorie. *Yellowstone* (Wonders of the World series). Raintree Steck-Vaughn Publishers, 1995. 64p. (gr. 6–7)

Blashfield, Jean F. *Antarctica* (Wonders of the World series). Raintree Steck-Vaughn Publishers, 1995. 64p. (gr. 6–7)

—. *Galápagos Islands*. Raintree Steck-Vaughn Publishers, 1995. 64p. (gr. 6–7)

Bonner, Nigel. *Polar Regions* (Habitats series). Thomson Learning, 1996. 48p. (gr. 4–6)

Brooks, Susan. *The Geography of the Earth*. Oxford University Press, 1996. (gr. 3–6)

Carpenter, Clive. *The Changing World of Weather*. Facts on File, 1991. (gr. 5+)

Catherall, Ed. *Exploring Soil and Rocks* (Exploring Science series). Steck-Vaughn Co., 1991. 48p. (gr. 4+)

Cheney, Glenn Alan. *Exploring Weather.* Steck-Vaughn Co., 1991. 48p. (gr. 4+)

Cumming, David. *Mountains* (Habitats series). Thomson Learning, 1996. 48p. (gr. 4–6)

—. *Rivers and Lakes.* Thomson Learning, 1996. 48p. (gr. 4–6)

Davies, Kay, and Wendy Oldfield. *The Super Science Book of Weather* (Super Science series). Thomson Learning, 1993. 32p. (gr. 4–8)

Dixon, Dougal. *The Changing Earth* (Young Geographer series). Thomson Learning, 1993. 32p. (gr. 4–6)

Dudman, John. *Earthquake* (Violent Earth series). Thomson Learning, 1993. 32p. (gr. 3–6)

—. *Volcano.* Thomson Learning, 1993. 32p. (gr. 3–6)

Dyson, Sue. *Wood* (Resources series). Thomson Learning, 1993. 32p. (gr. 3–6)

Fleisher, Paul. *Ecology A to Z.* Macmillan, 1994. 224p. (gr. 4+)

Flint, David. *The World's Weather* (Young Geographer series). Thomson Learning, 1993. 32p. (gr. 4–6)

Gutnik, Martin J., and Natalie Browne-Gutnik. *Great Barrier Reef* (Wonders of the World series). Raintree Steck-Vaughn Publishers, 1995. 64p. (gr. 6–7)

Jackman, Wayne. *Gas* (Resources series). Thomson Learning, 1993. 32p. (gr. 3–6)

—. *Plastics.* Thomson Learning, 1993. 32p. (gr. 3–6)

Jessop, Joanne. *Planet Earth* (New View series). Raintree Steck-Vaughn Publishers, 1994. 32p. (gr. 4–5)

Kerrod, Robin. *Energy Resources* (World's Resources). Thomson Learning, 1994. 32p. (gr. 4–7)

—. *Food Resources.* Thomson Learning, 1994. 32p. (gr. 4–7)

—. *Material Resources.* Thomson Learning, 1994. 32p. (gr. 4–7)

—. *Mineral Resources.* Thomson Learning, 1994. 32p. (gr. 4–7)

Knapp, Brian. *Drought* (World Disasters series). Steck-Vaughn Co., 1990. 48p. (gr. 5+)

—. *Earthquake.* Steck-Vaughn Co., 1990. 48p. (gr. 5+)

—. *Fire.* Steck-Vaughn Co., 1990. 48p. (gr. 5+)

—. *Flood.* Steck-Vaughn Co., 1990. 48p. (gr. 5+)

—. *Storm.* Steck-Vaughn Co., 1990. 48p. (gr. 5+)

—. *Volcano.* Steck-Vaughn Co., 1990. 48p. (gr. 5+)

Lambert, David. *Seas and Oceans* (New View series). Raintree Steck-Vaughn Publishers, 1994. 32p. (gr. 4–5)

Lucas, Eileen. *Everglades* (Wonders of the World series). Raintree Steck-Vaughn Publishers, 1995. 64p. (gr. 6–7)

Macdonald, Fiona. *Rain Forest* (New View series). Raintree Steck-Vaughn Publishers, 1994. 32p. (gr. 4–5)

McLeish, Ewan. *Wetlands* (Habitats series). Thomson Learning, 1996. 48p. (gr. 4–6)

Peacock, Graham. *Bricks* (Resources series). Thomson Learning, 1993. 32p. (gr. 3–6)

—. *The Super Science Book of Materials* (Super Science series). Thomson Learning, 1994. 32p. (gr. 4–8)

Pratt, Paula B. *Maps: Plotting Places on the Globe.* Lucent Books, 1994. 112p. (gr. 5–9)

Randle, Damian. *Natural Resources* (Young Geographer series). Thomson Learning, 1993. 32p. (gr. 4–6)

Rawlins, Carol. *Grand Canyon* (Wonders of the World series). Raintree Steck-Vaughn Publishers, 1995. 64p. (gr. 6–7)

Reed-King, Susan. *Food and Farming* (Young Geographer series). Thomson Learning, 1993. 32p. (gr. 4–6)

Rickard, Graham. *Oil* (Resources series). Thomson Learning, 1993. 32p. (gr. 3–6)

Simon, Seymour. *Oceans.* William Morrow, 1990. (gr. 4–6)

Snedden, Robert. *The Super Science Book of Rocks and Soils* (Super Science series). Thomson Learning, 1994. 32p. (gr. 4–8)

Stille, Darlene. *Soil Erosion and Pollution* (New True Book series). Children's Press, 1990. (gr. 4–6)

Van Rose, Susanna. *Volcano and Earthquake.* Knopf, 1992. 64p. (gr. 5+)

Waterlow, Julia. *Deserts* (Habitats series). Thomson Learning, 1996. 48p. (gr. 4–6)

—. *Flood* (Violent Earth series). Thomson Learning, 1993. 32p. (gr. 3–6)

—. *Islands* (Habitats series). Thomson Learning, 1996. 48p. (gr. 4–6)

—. *Journeys* (Young Geographer series). Thomson Learning, 1993. 32p. (gr. 4–6)

Weather: Drama from the Heavens. Abrams, 1996. (gr. 5–10)

Willis, Terri. *St. Lawrence River and Seaway* (Wonders of the World series). Raintree Steck-Vaughn Publishers, 1995. 64p. (gr. 6–7)

—. *Serengeti Plain.* Raintree Steck-Vaughn Publishers, 1995. 64p. (gr. 6–7)

—. *Sichuan Panda Forests.* Raintree Steck-Vaughn Publishers, 1995. 64p. (gr. 6–7)

Wood, Jenny. *Icebergs.* Puffin Books, 1990. (gr. 4+)

— *Storm* (Violent Earth series). Thomson Learning, 1994. 32p. (gr. 3–6)

Wood, Tim. *Natural Disasters* (The World's Disasters series). Thomson Learning, 1994. 48p. (gr. 4–6)

ENVIRONMENT/CONSERVATION

Atlas of the Environment. Raintree Steck-Vaughn Publishers, 1993. 96p. (gr. 4+)

Baines, John. *Acid Rain* (Conserving Our World series). Steck-Vaughn Co., 1990. 48p. (gr. 4–5)

—. *Conserving the Atmosphere.* Steck-Vaughn Co., 1990. 48p. (gr. 4–5)

—. *Environmental Disasters* (The World's Disasters series). Thomson Learning, 1994. 48p. (gr. 4–6)

—. *Exploring Humans and the Environment* (Exploring Science series). Raintree Steck-Vaughn Publishers, 1993. 48p. (gr. 4+)

—. *Protecting the Oceans.* Steck-Vaughn Co., 1991. 48p. (gr. 4–5)

Banks, Martin. *Conserving Rain Forests* (Conserving Our World series). Steck-Vaughn Co., 1990. 48p. (gr. 4–5)

Bramwell, Martyn. *The Environment and Conservation.* Prentice Hall, 1992. (gr. 4–6)

Bright, Michael. *Pollution and Wildlife.* Franklin Watts, 1992. 32p. (gr. 5–8)

Collinson, Alan. *Renewable Energy* (Facing the Future series). Steck-Vaughn Co., 1991. 48p. (gr. 5–6)

Duggleby, John. *Pesticides* (Earth Alert series). Crestwood, 1990. (gr. 5+)

Fishman, Jack. *Global Alert: The Ozone Pollution Crisis.* Plenum Press, 1990. (gr. 4–6)

Gay, Kathlyn. *Water Pollution.* Franklin Watts, 1990. (gr. 4–6)

Halpern, Robert R. *Green Planet Rescue: Saving the Earth's Endangered Plants.* Franklin Watts, 1993. 56p. (gr. 5–7)

Hamilton, John. *Eco-Careers* (Eco-Reference series). Abdo and Daughters, 1993. 32p. (gr. 4–6)

—. *Eco-Disasters.* Abdo and Daughters, 1993. 32p. (gr. 4–6)

—. *Eco-Groups.* Abdo and Daughters, 1993. 32p. (gr. 4–6)

Harlow, Rosie and Sally Morgan. *Energy and Power* (Kingfisher Young Discoverers series). Kingfisher Books, 1995. 32p. (gr. 4–6)

—. *Garbage and Recycling.* Kingfisher Books, 1995. 32p. (gr. 4–6)

—. *Nature in Danger.* Kingfisher Books, 1995. 32p. (gr. 4–6)

—. *Pollution and Waste.* Kingfisher Books, 1995. 32p. (gr. 4–6)

Harris, Colin. *Protecting the Planet* (Young Geographer series). Thomson Learning, 1993. 32p. (gr. 4–6)

Italia, Bob. *Earth Words* (Eco-Reference series). Abdo and Daughters, 1993. 64p. (gr. 4–6).

—. *Eco-Camping* (Eco-Activities series). Abdo and Daughters, 1993. 64p. (gr. 4–6)

James, Barbara. *Conserving the Polar Regions* (Conserving Our World series). Steck-Vaughn Co., 1991. 48p. (gr. 4–5)

—. *Waste and Recycling.* Steck-Vaughn Co., 1990. 48p. (gr. 4–5)

Kallen, Stuart. *Earth Keepers* (Eco-Reference series). Abdo and Daughters, 1993. 48p. (gr. 4–6)

—. *Eco-Arts and Crafts* (Eco-Activities series).

Abdo and Daughters, 1993. 48p. (gr. 4–6)

—. *Eco-Fairs and Carnivals.* Abdo and Daughters, 1993. 40p. (gr. 4–6)

—. *Eco-Games.* Abdo and Daughters, 1993. 32p. (gr. 4–6)

Lambert, David. *The World's Population* (Young Geographer series). Thomson Learning, 1993. 32p. (gr. 4–6)

Lambert, Mark. *Farming and the Environment* (Conserving Our World series). Steck-Vaughn Co., 1991. 48p. (gr. 4–5)

Lee, Sally. *Pesticides.* Franklin Watts, 1991. (gr. 5+)

McLeish, Ewan. *Spread of Deserts* (Conserving Our World series). Steck-Vaughn Co., 1991. 48p. (gr. 4–5)

Morgan, Sally. *The Super Science Book of the Environment.* (Super Science series). Thomson Learning, 1994. 32p. (gr. 4–8)

Owen, Oliver. *Eco-Solutions: It's in Your Hands.* Abdo and Daughters, 1993. 64p. (gr. 4–6)

—. *Intro to Your Environment.* Abdo and Daughters, 1993. 48p. (gr. 4–6)

Peacock, Graham and Terry Hudson. *Exploring Habitats* (Exploring Science series). Raintree Steck-Vaughn Publishers, 1993. 48p. (gr. 4+)

Penny, Malcolm. *Protecting Wildlife* (Conserving Our World series). Steck-Vaughn Co., 1991. 48p. (gr. 4–5)

Rescue Mission: Planet Earth. A Children's Edition of Agenda 21. Kingfisher Books, 1994. 96p. (gr. 4+)

Seidenberg, Steven. *Ecology and Conservation.* Gareth Stevens, 1990. (gr. 4–6)

Shepard, John. *The Stream Team on Patrol* (Eco-Activities series). Abdo and Daughters, 1993. 40p. (gr. 4–6)

Stille, Darlene. *Air Pollution.* Children's Press, 1990. (gr. 3–4)

—. *Water Pollution* (New True Books series). Children's Press, 1990. (gr. 4–6)

Wheeler, Jill. *Beastly Neighbors: A Book About Animals* (Eco-Resource series). Abdo and Daughters, 1993. 32p. (gr. 4–6)

—. *Branch Out: A Book About Land.* Abdo and Daughters, 1993. 32p. (gr. 4–6)

—. *Earth Kids.* Abdo and Daughters, 1993. 32p. (gr. 4–6)

—. *Every Drop Counts: A Book About Water.* Abdo and Daughters, 1993. 32p. (gr. 4–6)

—. *For the Birds: A Book About Air.* Abdo and Daughters, 1993. 32p. (gr. 4–6)

GENERAL SCIENCE

Cush, Cathie. *Disasters That Shook the World* (20 Events series). Raintree Steck-Vaughn Publishers, 1994. 48p. (gr. 5–6)

Davies, Kay and Wendy Oldfield. *The Super Science Book of Time* (Super Science series). Thomson Learning, 1993. 32p. (gr. 4–8)

Great Scientific Discoveries (Chambers Compact Reference series). Chambers, 1991. 256p. (gr. 7+)

The Kingfisher Science Encyclopedia. Kingfisher Books, 1991. 796p. (gr. 4+)

Larousse Dictionary of Science and Technology. Larousse, 1995. 1,248p. (gr. 7+)

Margulis, Lynn. *Diversity of Life: The Five Kingdoms.* Enslow, 1992. 80p. (gr. 6+)

Markham, Lois. *Discoveries That Changed Science* (20 Events series). Raintree Steck-Vaughn Publishers, 1995. 48p. (gr. 5–6)

Williams, Brian, et al. *Visual Encyclopedia of Science.* Larousse, 1994. 320p. (gr. 4+)

Watts, Lisa. *Science and Technology.* EDC/Usborne, 1996. (gr. 4+)

HEALTH SCIENCE/MEDICINE

ABC's of the Human Mind: A Family Answer Book. Reader's Digest, 1990. (gr. 4–6)

Ardley, Neil. *The Science Book of Light.* Harcourt Brace Jovanovich, 1991. (gr. 4–6)

Bishop, Pamela. *Exploring the Skeleton. Funny Bones and Not So Funny Bones.* Franklin Watts, 1991. (gr. 3–5)

Bryan, Jenny. *The History of Health and Medicine* (Science Discovery series). Thomson Learning, 1996. 48p. (gr. 6–9)

—. *Your Amazing Brain.* Reader's Digest Young Families/Wishing Well, 1996. (gr. 4–8)

Cohen, Philip. *Tobacco* (Drugs: The Complete Story series). Steck-Vaughn Co., 1992. 64p. (gr. 6+)

Facklam, Howard and Margery. *Viruses*. Twenty-first Century Books, 1994. 64p. (gr. 5–8)

Graham, Ian. *Fighting Disease* (Science Spotlight series). Raintree Steck-Vaughn Publishers, 1995. 48p. (gr. 6–7)

—. *Sports*. Raintree Steck-Vaughn Publishers, 1995. 48p. (gr. 6–7)

Harris, Jacqueline L. *Communicable Diseases*. Twenty-first Century Books, 1993. 64p. (gr. 5–8)

Holmes, Pamela. *Alcohol* (Drugs: The Complete Story series). Steck-Vaughn Co., 1992. 64p. (gr. 6+)

—. *Cocaine*. Steck-Vaughn Co., 1992. 64p. (gr. 6+)

Hooper, Tony. *Surgery* (Breakthrough series). Raintree Steck-Vaughn Publishers, 1994. 48p. (gr. 5–6)

Hyde, Margaret O. *Know About Drugs*. 3rd ed. Walker, 1990. 76p. (gr 3–7)

—. and Elizabeth Forsythe. *AIDS: What Does It Mean to You?* 4th ed. Walker, 1992. 128p. (gr. 7+)

Jukes, Mavis. *It's a Girl Thing: How to Stay Safe, Healthy, and In Charge*. Knopf, 1996. (gr. 5–8)

Landau, Elaine. *Cancer*. Twenty-first Century Books, 1994. 64p. (gr. 5–8)

Madison, Arnold. *Drugs and You*. Rev. ed. Messner, 1990. 114p. (gr. 7+)

Morris, Charles G. *Psychology: An Introduction*. 7th ed. Prentice Hall, 1990. (gr. 4–6)

Nardo, Don. *Germs: Mysterious Microorganisms*. Lucent Books, 1991. 96p. (gr. 5–8)

Parker, Steve. *Food and Digestion*. Franklin Watts, 1990. 48p. (gr. 5+)

—. *Heart and Blood*. Rev. ed. Franklin Watts, 1991. 48p. (gr. 5+)

Patent, Dorothy Hinshaw. *Nutrition: What's in the Food We Eat?* Holiday House, 1992. 40p. (gr. 3–7)

Pownall, Mark. *Heroin* (Drugs: The Complete Story series). Steck-Vaughn Co., 1992. 64p. (gr. 6+)

Saunderson, Jane. *Muscles and Bones*. Troll, 1992. 32p. (gr. 4–6)

Schmidt, R. and P. Adragna. *Human Anatomy and Physiology*. Saunders College Publishing, 1990. (gr. 4–6)

Schwartz, Linda. *AIDS: Questions and Answers for Kids*. Learning Works, 1993. 24p. (gr. 4–6)

Silverstein, Alvin, et. al. *Vitamins and Minerals*. Dorling Kindersley, 1991. 64p. (gr. 8+)

LIFE SCIENCE

Balkwill, Fran. *Amazing Schemes Within Your Genes*. Lerner, 1994. (gr. 3–6)

Bryan, Jenny. *Genetic Engineering* (Global Issues series). Thomson Learning, 1995. 64p. (gr. 7–9)

Byczynski, Lynn. *Genetics: Nature's Blueprints*. Lucent Books, 1991. 96p. (gr. 5–8)

Catherall, Ed. *Exploring the Human Body* (Exploring Science series). Raintree Steck-Vaughn Publishers, 1992. 48p. (gr. 4+)

Corbishley, Mike. *How Do We Know Where People Came From?* (How Do We Know? series). Raintree Steck-Vaughn Publishers, 1995. 48p. (gr. 5–6)

Dal Sasso, Cristiano. *Animals* (Beginnings—Origins and Evolution series). Raintree Steck-Vaughn Publishers, 1995. 48p. (gr. 6–7)

Darling, David. *Genetic Engineering: Redrawing the Genetic Blueprint of Life*. Silver Burdett, 1995. (gr. 5+)

Dixon, Dougal. *Prehistoric Life and Evolution*. Prentice-Hall, 1992.

Facchini, Fiorenzo. *Humans* (Beginnings—Origins and Evolution series). Raintree Steck-Vaughn Publishers, 1995. 48p. (gr. 6–7)

Facklam, Howard and Margery. *Bacteria*. Twenty-first Century Books, 1994. 64p. (gr. 5+)

Ganeri, Anita. *How Do We Know What's Inside Us?* (How Do We Know? series). Raintree Steck-Vaughn Publishers, 1995. 48p. (gr. 5–6)

Garassino, Alessandro. *Life* (Beginnings—Origins and Evolution series). Raintree Steck-Vaughn Publishers, 1995. 48p. (gr. 6–7)

Glover, David. *The Super Science Book of Life Processes*. (Super Science series). Thomson Learning, 1994. 32p. (gr. 4–8)

Hooper, Tony. *Genetics* (Breakthrough series). Raintree Steck-Vaughn Publishers, 1994. 48p. (gr. 5–6)

Peacock, Graham and Terry Hudson. *The Super Science Book of Our Bodies* (Super Science series). Thomson Learning, 1993. 32p. (gr. 4–8)

Place, Robin. *Bodies From the Past* (Digging Up the Past series). Thomson Learning, 1996. 48p. (gr. 4–6)

Ricciuti, Edward R. *Microorganisms: The Unseen World*. Blackbirch, 1994. 64p. (gr. 4–8)

Stefoff, Rebecca. *Extinction*. Chelsea House, 1991. (gr. 4–6)

Stephenson, Robert and Roger Browne. *Exploring Variety of Life* (Exploring Science series). Raintree Steck-Vaughn Publishers, 1993. 48p. (gr. 4+)

Taylor, Paul. *Fossil*. Random House, 1990. 64p. (gr. 5+)

Tessar, Jenny. *Humans*. Blackbirch, 1994. 64p. (gr. 4–8)

Winckler, S. and M. M. Rodgers. *Population Growth*. Lerner, 1991. (gr. 4–6)

Young, John K. *Cells: Amazing Forms and Functions*. Franklin Watts, 1990. (gr. 5+)

MATHEMATICS/COMPUTER SCIENCE

The Age of Computers. World Book, 1996. 64p. (gr. 4+)

Borman, Jami Lynne. *A Computer Dictionary for Kids...and Their Parents*. Barron, 1995. 256p. (gr. 4–8)

Cochrane, Kerry. *The Internet*. Franklin Watts, 1995. 64p. (gr. 4–6)

Darling, David. *Computers of the Future: Intelligent Machines and Virtual Reality*. Silver Burdett, 1995. (gr. 4+)

Embry, Lynn and Betty Bobo. *Math Around the World*. Good Apple, 1991. 144p. (gr. 4–6)

Feldman, Judy. *Shapes in Nature*. Children's Press, 1991. (gr. 3–5)

Fisher, Ann. *Intermediate Math Puzzlers*. Good Apple, 1994. 112p. (gr. 5–8)

Grahame, Ian. *Computers*. Franklin Watts, 1992. 32p. (gr. 5–8)

Narda, Don. *Computers: Mechanical Minds*. Lucent Books, 1990. 96p. (gr 5–8)

Osborne, Victor. *How Do We Know How to Measure?* (How Do We Know? series). Raintree Steck-Vaughn Publishers, 1995. 48p. (gr. 5–6)

Pallas, Norvin. *Calculator Puzzles, Tricks, and Games*. Dover, 1991. 96p. (gr. 4–6)

Parker, Charles. *Understanding Computers and Information Processing*. Dryden Press, 1990. (gr. 6–8)

Pederson, Ted and Francis Moss. *The Internet for Kids: A Beginner's Guide to Surfing the Net*. Price Stern Sloan, 1995. 206p. (gr. 4–10)

Sachar, Louis. *Sideways Arithmetic from Wayside School*. Scholastic, 1992. 96p. (gr. 4–8)

Smoothey, Marian. *Let's Investigate Calculators*. Marshall Cavendish, 1992. 64p. (gr. 4–8)

—. *Let's Investigate Estimating*. Marshall Cavendish, 1992. 64p. (gr. 4–8)

—. *Let's Investigate Graphs*. Marshall Cavendish, 1992. 64p. (gr. 4–8)

—. *Let's Investigate Ratio and Proportion*. Marshall Cavendish, 1992. 64p. (gr. 4–8)

Stevens, M. *Computer for Beginners*. EDC Publishing, 1995. 48p. (gr. 4+)

VanCleave, Janice. *Janice VanCleave's Math for Every Kid: Easy Activities That Make Learning Math Fun*. Wiley, 1991. 215p. (gr. 4–6)

Watts, L. and L. Inglis. *Computers*. EDC Publishing, 1993. 32p. (gr. 3–9)

Wyler, Rose. *Math Fun with Money Puzzlers*. Simon and Schuster, 1992. (gr. 4–7)

—. *Math Fun with Tricky Lines and Shapes*. Simon and Schuster, 1992. (gr. 4–7)

PHYSICS/CHEMISTRY

Asimov, Isaac. *How Did We find Out About Lasers?* Walker, 1990. (gr. 3–5)

Bardon, Keith. *Exploring Forces and Structures* (Exploring Science series). Raintree Steck-Vaughn Publishers, 1992. 48p. (gr. 4+)

Biel, Timothy L. *Atom: Building Blocks of Matter*. Lucent Books, 1990. 96p. (gr. 5–8)

Catherall, Ed. *Exploring Electricity* (Exploring Science series). Steck-Vaughn Co., 1990. 48p. (gr. 4+)

—. *Exploring Energy Sources.* Steck-Vaughn Co., 1991. 48p. (gr. 4+)

—. *Exploring Light.* Steck-Vaughn Co., 1990. 48p. (gr. 4+)

—. *Exploring Magnets.* Steck-Vaughn Co., 1990. 48p. (gr. 4+)

—. *Exploring Sound.* Steck-Vaughn Co., 1990. 48p. (gr. 4+)

—. *Exploring Uses of Energy.* Steck-Vaughn Co., 1991. 48p. (gr. 4+)

Chambers Nuclear Energy and Radiation Dictionary. W & R Chambers, 1992. 352p. (gr. 7+)

Dunn, Andrew. *Heat* (How Things Work series). Thomson Learning, 1993. 32p. (gr. 3–6)

—. *It's Electric.* Thomson Learning, 1993. 32p. (gr. 3–6)

—. *Lifting By Levers.* Thomson Learning, 1993. 32p. (gr. 3–6)

—. *The Power of Pressure.* Thomson Learning, 1993. 32p. (gr. 3–6)

—. *Simple Slopes.* Thomson Learning, 1993. 32p. (gr. 3–6)

—. *Wheels at Work.* Thomson Learning, 1993. 32p. (gr. 3–6)

Gardner, Robert. *Experimenting with Light.* Franklin Watts, 1991. (gr. 3–5)

Glover, David. *Batteries, Bulbs, and Wires* (Kingfisher Young Discoverers series). Kingfisher Books, 1993. 32p. (gr. 4–6)

—. *Flying and Floating.* Kingfisher Books, 1993. 32p. (gr. 4–6)

—. *Solids and Liquids.* Kingfisher Books, 1993. 32p. (gr. 4–6)

—. *Sound and Light.* Kingfisher Books, 1993. 32p. (gr. 4–6)

—. *The Super Science Book of Sound* (Super Science series). Thomson Learning, 1994. 32p. (gr. 4–8)

Grahame, Ian. *Lasers and Holograms.* Franklin Watts, 1991. 32p. (gr. 5–8)

Hooper, Tony. *Electricity* (Breakthrough series). Raintree Steck-Vaughn Publishers, 1994. 48p. (gr. 5–6)

Jennings, Terry. *How Do We Know Energy Exists?* (How Do We Know? series). Raintree Steck-Vaughn Publishers, 1995. 48p. (gr. 5–6)

Langley, Andrew. *Paper* (Resources series). Thomson Learning, 1993. 32p. (gr. 3–6)

—. *Steel.* Thomson Learning, 1993. 32p. (gr. 3–6)

Lloyd, Gill, and David Jefferis. *The History of Optics.* (Science Discovery series). Thomson Learning, 1995. 48p. (gr. 6–9)

Newmark, Ann. *Chemistry.* Dorling Kindersley, 1993. 64p. (gr. 7+)

Peacock, Graham and Terry Hudson. *The Super Science Book of Light.* (Super Science series). Thomson Learning, 1993. 32p. (gr. 4–8)

—. *Electricity* (Resources series). Thomson Learning, 1993. 32p. (gr. 3–6)

Sonhurst, Hazel. *Glass* (Resources series). Thomson Learning, 1993. 32p. (gr. 3–6)

Snedden, Robert. *The History of Electricity* (Science Discovery series). Thomson Learning, 1995. 48p. (gr. 6–9)

Taylor, Barbara. *Color and Light.* Franklin Watts, 1990. 32p. (gr. 3–6)

Wellington, Jerry. *The Super Science Book of Energy* (Super Science series). Thomson Learning, 1994. 32p. (gr. 4–8)

—. *The Super Science Book of Forces.* Thomson Learning, 1994. 32p. (gr. 4–8)

PLANTS

Bennett, Paul. *Pollinating a Flower* (Nature's Secrets series). Thomson Learning, 1994. 32p. (gr. 3–5)

Bown, Deni. *Orchids* (The Green World series). Steck-Vaughn Co., 1992. 48p. (gr. 5+)

Catherall, Ed. *Exploring Plants* (Exploring Science series). Raintree Steck-Vaughn Publishers, 1992. 48p. (gr. 4+)

Cochrane, Jennifer. *Food Plants* (The Green World series). Steck-Vaughn Co., 1991. 48p. (gr. 5+)

—. *Trees of the Tropics.* Steck-Vaughn Co., 1991. 48p. (gr. 5+)

Coil, Suzanne M. *Poisonous Plants.* Franklin Watts, 1992. 64p. (gr. 5–8)

Ganeri, Anita. *Plant Science.* Silver Burdett, 1993. 48p. (gr. 5+)

Garassino, Alessandro. *Plants* (Beginnings—Origins and Evolution series). Raintree Steck-Vaughn Publishers, 1995. 48p. (gr. 6–7)

Greenaway, Theresa. *Ferns* (The Green World series). Steck-Vaughn Co., 1992. 48p. (gr. 5+)

—. *Fir Trees.* Steck-Vaughn Co., 1990. 48p. (gr. 5+)

—. *First Plants.* Steck-Vaughn Co., 1991. 48p. (gr. 5+)

—. *Grasses and Grains.* Steck-Vaughn Co., 1990. 48p. (gr. 5+)

—. *Mosses and Liverworts.* Steck-Vaughn Co., 1992. 48p. (gr. 5+)

—. *Woodland Trees.* Steck-Vaughn Co., 1991. 48p. (gr. 5+)

Landau, Elaine. *Endangered Plants.* Franklin Watts, 1992. 64p. (gr. 5–8)

Madgwick, Wendy. *Cacti and Other Succulents* (The Green World series). Steck-Vaughn Co., 1992. 48p. (gr. 5+)

—. *Flowering Plants.* Steck-Vaughn Co., 1990. 48p. (gr. 5+)

—. *Fungi and Lichens.* Steck-Vaughn Co., 1990. 48p. (gr. 5+)

Mutel, C.F. and M. M. Rodgers. *Tropical Rainforests.* (Our Endangered World series) Lerner, 1991. (gr. 3–5)

Nielsen, Nancy J. *Carnivorous Plants.* Franklin Watts, 1992. 64p. (gr. 5–8)

Owen, Oliver. *Acorn to Oak Tree* (Lifewatch: The Mystery of Nature series). Abdo and Daughters, 1994. 32p. (gr. 4–6)

—. *Bulb to Tulip.* Abdo and Daughters, 1995. 32p. (gr. 4–6)

—. *Seed to Peanut.* Abdo and Daughters, 1995. 32p. (gr. 4–6)

Pope, Joyce. *Plant Partnerships.* Facts on File, 1991. 62p. (gr. 6+)

SPACE AND THE UNIVERSE

Apfel, Necia H. *Voyager to the Planets.* Clarion, 1991. (gr. 3–5)

Couper, Heather and Nigel Henbest. *Black Holes.* Dorling Kindersley, 1996. (gr. 6+)

Curtis, Neil. *How Do We Know the Earth Is Round?* (How Do We Know? series). Raintree Steck-Vaughn Publishers, 1995. 48p. (gr. 5–6)

Exploring Outer Space: Rockets, Probes, and Satellites. Rev. ed. Ed. by Isaac Asimov, et. al. Gareth Stevens, 1995. (gr. 3+)

Graham, Ian. *Astronomy* (Science Spotlight series). Raintree Steck-Vaughn Publishers, 1995. 48p. (gr. 6–7)

—. *Spacecraft* (Pointers series). Raintree Steck-Vaughn Publishers, 1994. 32p. (gr. 4–5)

—. *Space Science* (Facing the Future series). Raintree Steck-Vaughn Publishers, 1993. 48p. (gr. 5–6)

Lambert, David. *Stars and Planets* (New View series). Raintree Steck-Vaughn Publishers, 1994. 32p. (gr. 4–5)

Miotto, Enrico. *The Universe* (Beginnings—Origins and Evolution series). Raintree Steck-Vaughn Publishers, 1995. 48p. (gr. 6–7)

Muirden, James. *How Do We Know About the Universe?* (How Do We Know? series). Raintree Steck-Vaughn Publishers, 1995. 48p. (gr. 5–6)

Nicolson, Iain. *Explore the World of Space and the Universe.* Western Publishing, 1992. 48p. (gr. 3–7)

Peacock, Graham. *The Super Science Book of Space* (Super Science series). Thomson Learning, 1994. 32p. (gr. 4–8)

Pfister, Marcus. *Sun and Moon.* Gareth Stevens, 1993. (gr. 4–7)

Space Exploration (Chambers Compact Reference series). Chambers, 1992. 256p. (gr. 7+)

Stannard, Russell. *Our Universe: A Guide to What's Out There.* Kingfisher Books, 1995. 96p. (gr. 3–8)

Stars and Planets. Time Life Kids, 1996. (gr. 3–7)

Steele, Philip. *Astronomy.* Macmillan, 1991. 32p. (gr. 5–6)

—. *Black Holes and Other Space Phenomena* (Young Observer series). Kingfisher Books, 1995. 40p. (gr. 3–6)

Stephenson, Robert and Roger Browne. *Exploring Earth in Space* (Exploring Science series). Raintree Steck-Vaughn Publishers, 1992. 48p. (gr. 4+)

Wellington, Jerry. *The History of Space* (Science Discovery series). Thomson Learning, 1996.

48p. (gr. 6–9)

Wulforst, Harry. *The Rocketmakers*. Orion, 1990. (gr. 5+)

TECHNOLOGY/ENGINEERING

Barber, Nicola. *Building for Tomorrow* (Facing the Future series). Raintree Steck-Vaughn Publishers, 1993. 48p. (gr. 5–6)

Berliner, Don. *Aviation: Reaching for the Sky*. Oliver, 1996. (gr. 5+)

Bowler, Mike. *Trains* (Pointers series). Raintree Steck-Vaughn Publishers, 1995. 32p. (gr. 4–5)

Bridgmen, Roger. *Electronics*. Dorling Kindersley, 1993. 64p. (gr. 3–6)

Cooper, Alan. *Rail Travel* (World on the Move series). Thomson Learning, 1993. 32p. (gr. 5–9)

Cross, Robin. *Technology of War* (World War II series). Thomson Learning, 1994. 48p. (gr. 5–9)

Davies, Eryl. *Water Travel* (World on the Move series). Thomson Learning, 1993. 32p. (gr. 5–9)

Dunn, Andrew. *Bridges* (Structures series). Thomson Learning, 1993. 32p. (gr. 5–8)

—. *Dams*. Thomson Learning, 1993. 32p. (gr. 5–8)

—. *Skyscrapers*. Thomson Learning, 1993. 32p. (gr. 5–8)

—. *Tunnels*. Thomson Learning, 1993. 32p. (gr. 5–8)

Gardner, Robert. *Experimenting with Inventions*. Franklin Watts, 1990. (gr. 4–6)

Gates, Phil. *Nature Got There First: Inventions Inspired by Nature*. Kingfisher Books, 1995. 80p. (gr. 3–8)

Graeme, J. et al. *Many Ways to Travel* (Hand in Hand series). Addison-Wesley, 1990. (gr. 5+)

Graham, Ian. *Boats, Ships, Submarines* (How Things Work series). Raintree Steck-Vaughn Publishers, 1993. 40p. (gr. 3–7)

—. *Cars* (Pointers series). Raintree Steck-Vaughn Publishers, 1994. 32p. (gr. 4–5)

—. *Cars, Bikes, Trains* (How Things Work series). Raintree Steck-Vaughn Publishers, 1993. 40p. (gr. 3–7)

—. *Crime-Fighting* (Science Spotlight series). Raintree Steck-Vaughn Publishers, 1995. 48p. (gr. 6–7)

—. *Fakes and Forgeries*. Raintree Steck-Vaughn Publishers, 1995. 48p. (gr. 6–7)

—. *Stage and Screen*. Raintree Steck-Vaughn Publishers, 1995. 48p. (gr. 6–7)

—. *Transportation* (Facing the Future series). Raintree Steck-Vaughn Publishers, 1993. 48p. (gr. 5–6)

Great Inventions Through History (Chambers Compact Reference series). Chambers, 1991. 256p. (gr. 7+)

Great Modern Inventions. (Chambers Compact Reference series). Chambers, 1991. 256p. (gr. 7+)

Hill, John. *Exploring Information Technology* (Exploring Science series). Raintree Steck-Vaughn Publishers, 1993. 48p. (gr. 4+)

Humble, Richard. *Ships* (Pointers series). Raintree Steck-Vaughn Publishers, 1994. 32p. (gr. 4–5)

Jackson, Donna. *How Forensic Anthropologists Solve Crimes and Uncover Mysteries of the Dead*. Little, Brown, 1996. (gr. 4+)

Jaspersohn, Jasper. *Timber: From Trees to Wood Products*. Little, Brown, 1996. (gr. 3–6)

Jay, Michael. *The History of Communications* (Science Discovery series). Thomson Learning, 1995. 48p. (gr. 6–9)

Jennings, Terry. *Cranes, Dump Trucks, Bulldozers* (How Things Work series). Kingfisher Books, 1993. 40p. (gr. 3–7)

Jones, Charlotte F. *Accidents May Happen: Fifty Inventions Discovered by Mistake*. Delacorte, 1996. (gr. 4+)

—. *Mistakes That Worked*. Doubleday, 1994. (gr. 4–7)

Lafferty, Peter. *The Inventor Through History* (Journey Through History series). Thomson Learning, 1993. 48p. (gr. 5–8)

Markham, Lois. *Inventions That Changed Modern Life* (20 Events series). Raintree Steck-Vaughn Publishers, 1994. 48p. (gr. 5–6)

McKenzie, Ian. *The History of Criminal Investigation* (Science Discovery series).

Thomson Learning, 1996. 48p. (gr. 6–9)

Munro, Bob. *Aircraft* (Pointers series). Raintree Steck-Vaughn Publishers, 1994. 32p. (gr. 4–5)

O'Reilly, Susan. *Textiles*. Franklin Watts, 1991. 48p. (gr. 5–8)

Parker, Steven. *The Flying Bedstead and Other Ingenious Inventions* (Young Observer series). Kingfisher Books, 1995. 40p. (gr. 3–6)

Rowe, Julian. *Science and Technology* (Legacies series). Thomson Learning, 1996. 48p. (gr. 4–6)

Salter, Andrew. *Trucks* (Pointers series). Raintree Steck-Vaughn Publishers, 1995. 32p. (gr. 4–5)

Sauvain, Philip. *Communications* (Breakthrough series). Raintree Steck-Vaughn Publishers, 1994. 48p. (gr. 5–6)

Singer, Donna. *Structures That Changed the Way the World Looked* (20 Events series). Raintree Steck-Vaughn Publishers, 1995. 48p. (gr. 5–6)

Skurzyski, Gloria. *Robots: Your Hi-Tech World.* Bradbury Press, 1990. (gr. 4–6)

Snedden, Robert. *The History of Genetics* (Science Discovery series). Thomson Learning, 1995. 48p. (gr. 6–9)

Steins, Richard. *Transportation Milestones and Breakthroughs* (20 Events series). Raintree Steck-Vaughn Publishers, 1995. 48p. (gr. 5–6)

Tanaka, Shelly. *The Disaster of the Hindenburg: The Last Flight of the Greatest Airship Ever Built.* Scholastic, 1996. (gr. 3–6)

Transportation and Communications. Time-Life, 1990. (gr. 5+)

Visual Dictionary of Ships and Sailing. Dorling Kindersley, 1991. (gr. 5+)

Wilcox, Charlotte. *Powerhouse: Inside a Nuclear Power Plant.* Lerner/First Avenue Editions, 1996. (gr. 3–6)

Williams, Brian. *The History of Transportation* (Science Discovery series). Thomson Learning, 1996. 48p. (gr. 6–9)

Wood, Tim. *Air Travel* (World on the Move series). Thomson Learning, 1993. 32p. (gr. 5–9)

—. *Road Travel.* Thomson Learning, 1993. 32p. (gr. 5–9)

CD–ROMs
Animals
African Wild Animal Adventures. Mac, Windows. Abdo and Daughters, 1995. (gr. 4–5)

Ask About Endangered Species. Windows. William K. Bradford Publishing Co., Inc. (gr. 4–9)

Children's Atlas World of Wildlife. Windows. Rand McNally. (gr. 3–8)

Eyewitness Virtual Reality Bird. Windows. Dorling Kindersley. (gr. 5+)

In the Company of Whales. Windows. Discovery Communications, Inc., 1993. (gr. 4+)

Media Factor—Mammals. Windows. Andromeda Interactive Limited, 1995. (gr. 4+)

Microsoft Dogs. Windows. Microsoft. (gr. 3–12)

Multimedia Cats from Inroad Interactive. Windows. Broderbund Software, Inc. (gr. 4–9)

Multimedia Dogs. Windows. Broderbund Software, Inc. (gr. 4–9)

The San Diego Zoo Presents...the Animals. Mac, DOS. Software Toolworks. (gr. 3+)

Scavenger Hunt Adventure Series: Africa. Mac, Windows. Davidson & Associates, Inc. (gr. 3–12)

Sharks! An Interactive Journey. Mac, Windows. The Discovery Channel. (gr. 5+)

Sim Ant®. Windows. Maxis. (gr. 4–12)

Whales and Their Environment. Windows. Sunburst Communications, Inc. (gr. 4–8)

Dinosaurs
Ask About Dinosaurs. Windows. William K. Bradford Publishing Co., Inc. (gr. 4–9)

Microsoft Dinosaurs. Windows. Microsoft. (gr. 3–12)

World of Dinosaurs Reading Program. Macintosh. Raintree Steck-Vaughn Publishers, 1994. (gr. 3–4)

Earth Science
Ecosystems. Windows. Sunburst Communications, Inc. (gr. 4–8)

Maps and Navigation. Windows. Sunburst Communications, Inc. (gr. 4–8)

Microsoft Oceans. Windows. Microsoft. (gr. 3–12)

Odell Down Under. Mac, Windows. MECC. (gr. 4+)

Operation Weather Disaster. Mac, Windows. The

Discovery Channel Multimedia. (gr. 4+)

Projects for the Real World: Desert Survival. Windows. Wasatch Education Systems. (gr. 3–5)

Violent Earth Interactive Science Program. Mac, Windows. Raintree Steck-Vaughn Publishers, 1996. (gr. 4–6)

Weather Workstation. Windows. William K. Bradford Publishing Co., Inc. (gr. 6–9)

World Vista™. Windows. Rand McNally. (gr. 5–12)

Environment/Conservation

Last Chance to See. Windows. The Voyager Company. (gr. 5–12)

General Science

Science Discovery. Windows. Computer Curriculum Corporation. (gr. 6–9)

The Virtual Bio Park. Windows. Computer Curriculum Corporation. (gr. 5–9)

What's the Secret, Vols. 1 and 2. Mac, Windows. 3M Learning Software. (gr. 3–7)

Health Science/Medicine

A.D.A.M. The Inside Story. Mac, Windows. A.D.A.M. Software. (gr. 5+)

AnnaTommy. Windows. IVI Publishing. (gr. 5–9)

How Your Body Works. Windows. Mindscape. (gr. 4–12)

Mayo Clinic Family Health Book. IVI Publishing. (gr. 5–12)

The Virtual Body. Windows. IVI Publishing. (gr. 4–10)

Life Science

Biology Explorer: Genetics. Logical Software, Inc. (gr. 7+)

Sim Life®. Mac, DOS. Maxis. (gr. 8+)

Mathematics/Computer Science

Counting on Frank. Mac, Windows. Creative Wonders. (gr. 5–7)

How Multimedia Computers Work. Windows. Mindscape. (gr. 5+)

Math Ace. Windows. Magic Quest. (gr. 3–9)

Math Links. Mac, DOS. Logo Computer Systems. (gr. 4–8)

Maya Math. Windows. Sunburst Communications, Inc. (gr. 4–8)

Super Solvers OutNumbered! Windows. The Learning Company. (gr. 3–5)

Physics/Chemistry

Chemistry Explorer: The Atom. Windows. Logical Software, Inc. (gr. 7+)

Chemistry Explorer: Gas Laws. Windows. Logical Software, Inc. (gr. 7+)

Physics Explorer: Diffraction and Interference. Windows. Logical Software, Inc. (gr. 7+)

Physics Explorer: Waves. Windows. Logical Software, Inc. (gr. 7+)

Super Solvers Gizmos and Gadgets. DOS. The Learning Company. (gr. 3–7)

Wild Science Arcade. DOS. Binary Zoo. (gr. 3–9)

Plants

Biology Explorer: Photosynthesis. Windows. Logical Software, Inc. (gr. 7+)

Coral Kingdom. Windows. Sunburst Communications, Inc. (gr. 8+)

Investigating Plant Science. Windows. Attica Cybernetics, Inc. (gr. 7+)

Space and the Universe

A Field Trip to the Sky. Windows. Sunburst Communications, Inc. (gr. 4–8)

For All Mankind. Windows. The Voyager Company. (gr. 4–12)

The Interactive Space Ecyclopedia. Windows. Andromeda Interactive Limited, 1993. (gr. 5+)

Media Factor—Space. Windows. Andromeda Interactive Limited, 1995. (gr. 4+)

Planetary Taxi. Windows. The Voyager Company. (gr. 3–12)

Red Shift 2. Mac, Windows. Maxis. (gr. 6+)

Space Adventure II. Windows. Knowledge Adventures, Inc. (gr. 3–6)

Technology/Engineering

Aviation Adventure. Windows. Knowledge Adventures, Inc. (gr. 4–7)

Even More Incredible Machine. DOS. Sierra On-line, Inc. (gr. 3+)

Inventor Labs. Mac, Windows. Houghton Mifflin Interactive. (gr. 5+)

Media Factor—Cars. Windows. Andromeda Interactive Limited, 1995. (gr. 4+)

Microsoft World of Flight. Windows. Microsoft. (gr. 3–12)

INDEX

The index makes it easy for you to find any subject in the *Raintree Steck-Vaughn Illustrated Science Encyclopedia*. For example, the **bold** numbers **1:19-20** after the Acid rain entry tell you that there is an article on that subject in Volume 1, pages 19 and 20. The numbers in regular type, 16:1492, tell you that acid rain is mentioned in another article in Volume 16, page 1492. The *italic* numbers, *1:20*, mean that there is an illustration on the page indicated. For example, there is an illustration of acid rain in Volume 1, page 20.

Air brake, 3:246
Aircraft carrier, *18:1724*
Air-cushion vehicle, **1:46**, *1:46*
Airfoil, 1:30, **1:46-47**, *1:46*
Air mass, **1:47**
Airplane, *1:28*, 1:30, *1:30*, **1:48-51**, *1:48-51*, *1:52*, *2:160*, 8:730, 9:794, *11:1014*, *12:1120*, 16:1453, *16:1531*, *18:1726*, *19:1801*, *20:1873*, *21:1937*, *21:1946*, 22:2098
Airport, **1:52-53**, *1:52-53*, *17:1568*
Air pollution, 1:44, *1:44*, 19:1757, 19:1758
Air pressure, 1:43, 22:2068
Airship, 2:161, *2:161*, *2:172*, *10:946. See also* Dirigible.
Albatross, **1:54**, *1:54*
Albino, **1:54**, *1:54*
Alchemy, **1:54-55**, *4:351*
Alcohol, **1:55**, 7:661, 7:662
Alcoholism, **1:55**
Alder, **1:56**, *1:56*
Alewife, **1:56**
Alfalfa, **1:56**, *1:56*
Algae, 1:34, **1:57-58**, *1:57-58*, 12:1072, *15:1440*, 18:1680, 18:1704, 21:1929
Algebra, **1:59-60**, *1:59-60*
Alimentary canal, **1:61**, *1:61*
Alkali, **1:61-62**, *1:62*, 12:1117
Alkali metal, **1:62**
Alkaline earth metal, **1:62**
Alkaloid, **1:62-63**
Allele, **1:63**
Allergy, **1:63-64**, *1:63*, 2:106, 10:882, 10:912
Alligator, **1:64**, *1:64*
Alloy, **1:64-66**, *1:66*, 3:247, 5:447, 14:1310
Alluvium, **1:66**, *1:66*
Almond, **1:67**, *1:67*
Aloe, **1:67**, *1:67*, 22:2102
Alpha Centauri, **1:67-68**
Alpha particle, 1:15, **1:68**, 18:1670

Alternating current, **1:68**, *1:68*, 5:473, 17:1608
Alternation of generations, **1:68-69**, *1:69*
Altimeter, **1:69**, *1:69*
Altitude, **1:69-70**
Alum, **1:70**
Alumina, 1:9
Aluminum, **1:70-71**, *1:70-71*, 2:184
Alvarez, Luis, **1:71**
Alzheimer's disease, **1:72**
Amalgam, **1:72**
Amanita, *9:773*
Amaranth family, **1:72**, *1:72*
Amaryllis family, **1:73**, *1:73*
Amazonite, *13:1221*
Amber, **1:73**
Ameba, **1:73**, *1:73*, 7:670, *17:1542*
Amethyst, **1:74**, *1:74*
Amine, **1:74**
Amino acid, **1:74-75**, *16:1536*
Ammeter, **1:75**, *1:75*
Ammonia, *1:11*, **1:76**, 14:1312, 14:1313
Ammonite, **1:76**, *1:76*, *4:336*
Amniocentesis, **1:76-77**
Ampere, **1:77**
Ampère, André, **1:77**
Amphetamine, **1:77**
Amphibian, **1:78-79**, *1:78-79*, *15:1381*, *21:2011. See also* specific types.
Amphioxus, *14:1319*
Amplifier, **1:80**
Amplitude, **1:80**, *1:80*
Anaconda, **1:80-81**, *1:80*
Anaerobe, **1:81**
Anaerobic respiration, **1:81**
Analgesic, **1:81**
Analog, *1:81*
Anatomy, **1:82-85**, *1:82-85*
Anchovy, **1:86**
Andrews, Roy Chapman, **1:86**
Android, **1:86**, *1:86*
Andromeda galaxy, *9:781*
Anemia, **1:86**, 19:1733
Anemometer, **1:87**, *1:87*

Anesthetic, **1:87**, 4:363, 16:1529, 20:1875
Aneurysm, **1:87**
Angelfish, **1:88**
Anglerfish *1:12*
Angiography, **1:88**
Angioplasty, **1:88**
Angiosperm, **1:88-89**, *1:89*, 14:1253
Angstrom unit, **1:89**
Anhydride, **1:89**
Aniline, **1:89**
Animal breeding, 3:252, 18:1709
Animal kingdom, **1:90-91**, *1:90-91*, 4:377, 23:2134-35. *See also* specific types of animals.
Anion, **1:92**, 11:1001
Annealing, **1:92**
Annelida, **1:92**, *1:92*
Annual plant, **1:93**, *1:93*
Annual ring, **1:93**, *1:93*
Anodizing, **1:93-94**
Anorexia nervosa, **1:94**, 3:264
Ant, **1:94-95**, *1:94*, *11:982*
Anteater, **1:95**, *1:95*, *7:581*
Antelope, **1:95-96**, 7:596, 9:835, 10:880, 11:965, *11:965*, *18:1668*, *19:1818*, *21:1986*
Antenna, **1:96**, *1:96*, *5:419*, 17:1580, 20:1909
Antennae, **2:101**, *2:101*
Anther, **2:101**, *2:101*
Antheridium, **2:101**
Anthropoid, **2:102**, *2:102*
Anthropology, **2:102**
Antibiotic, **2:102-3**, 15:1405
Antibody, **2:103-4**, 10:959, 18:1713
Anticline, **2:104**, *2:104*, *8:732*
Anticyclone, **2:105**, *2:105*
Antidote, **2:105**
Antifreeze, **2:105-6**
Antigen, 2:103
Antihistamine, **2:106**
Antimatter, **2:106**
Antiparticle, 2:106

B

Babbage, Charles, **2:165**
Baboon, **2:165**, *2:165, 5:415, 16:1520*
Backswimmer, **2:165-66**, *2:166*
Bacon, Francis, **2:166**, *2:166*
Bacteria, **2:166-68**, *2:167,* 6:531, *7:620, 13:1203,* 18:1639, 18:1644, 18:1689, 20:1854, 21:1974, 21:1983
Bacteriophage, **2:168**
Badger, **2:168-69**, *2:168*
Baekeland, Leo, **2:169**
Bakelite, **2:169**
Balance, **2:169**, *2:169*
Bald eagle, **2:169-70**, *2:170*
Ball bearing, 2:186
Ballistics, **2:170-71**
Balloon, *1:44, 2:159,* **2:171-73**, *2:171-73,* 17:1585
Balsam, **2:173**, *2:173*
Bamboo, **2:173-74**, *2:173*
Banana, **2:174**, *2:174*
Bandicoot, **2:174**, *2:174, 13:1158*
Banneker, Benjamin, **2:174-75**
Banting, Sir Fredrick Grant, **2:175**
Banyan, **2:175**, *2:175*
Baobab, *21:1968*
Barbary ape, *5:418*
Barberry family, **2:175-76**, *2:175*
Barbiturate, **2:176**
Barium, **2:176**
Bark, **2:176-77**, *2:177*
Barley, *1:36, 1:37,* **2:177**, *2:177, 22:2072*
Barnacle, **2:178**, *2:178*
Barnard, Christiaan Neethling, **2:178**
Barometer, **2:178-79**, *2:178, 13:1197*
Barracuda, **2:179**, *2:179*
Basalt, **2:179-80**, *2:179*
Base, 1:61, **2:180**, 14:1305, 15:1419

Base code, **2:180**
Basket star, **2:180**, *2:180*
Bass, **2:181**, *2:181*
Bat, **2:181-82**, *2:181-82, 8:721, 10:909, 11:985, 14:1315,* 21:1998, *21:1998,* 22:2090
Bathysphere and bathyscaphe, **2:182-83**, *2:182,* 6:537, 16:1445
Battery, **2:183-84**, *2:183-84,* 4:329, *4:329*
Baud, **2:184**
Bauxite, 1:70, **2:184-85**, *2:144*
Bayberry, **2:185**, *2:185*
Beadle, George Wells, **2:185**
Beak, **2:185**, *2:185*
Bean, **2:185-86**, *8:760, 12:1062*
Bear, **2:186**, *2:186, 3:224, 3:257, 9:855,* 11:1028, *11:1028,* 16:1485, *19:1805,* 20:1869
Bearing, **2:186-87**
Beaufort scale, **2:187**, *2:187*
Beaver, **2:188-89**, *2:188*
Becquerel, Antoine Henri, **2:189**
Bedbug, **2:189**, *2:189*
Bedrock, **2:189**
Bee, **2:189-92**, *2:189-91, 13:1219, 16:1490, 22:2063*
Beech family, **2:192**, *2:192*
Beefalo, 3:223
Beet, 3:204. *See also* Sugar beet.
Beetle, *2:101,* **3:197**, *3:197, 4:361, 4:378, 4:378, 5:411, 5:411, 6:490, 6:493, 6:560, 11:980, 11:982, 11:983, 11:1032,* 18:1688, 22:2083
Begonia, *3:197, 3:197,* 10:899
Behavior of animals, **3:198-99**, *3:198-99*
Bell, Alexander Graham, **3:200**, *3:200*
Benthos, **3:200**, *3:200*
Benz, Karl, **3:200**
Benzene, **3:201**, *3:201,* 10:942, *10:942,* 11:1021
Beriberi, **3:201**

Bernoulli effect, **3:202**, *3:202*
Bernoulli family, **3:202**
Berry, **3:202-203**, *3:202*
Beryl, **3:203**, *3:203*
Berzelius, Jöns Jakob, **3:203**
Bessemer, Sir Henry, **3:203**
Beta-blocker, **3:203**
Beta particle, **3:204**, 18:1670
Biceps, **3:204**, *3:204*
Biennial plant, **3:204**, *3:204*
Big bang theory, **3:205**, *3:205, 3:225*
Big Dipper and Little Dipper, **3:205-206**, *3:206*
Bile, **3:206**
Bimetallic strip, **3:206**, 21:1932, *21:1933,* 21:1934, *21:1934*
Binary numbers, **3:206**
Binary star, **3:207**, *3:207*
Bindweed, **3:207-208**, *3:208*
Binet, Alfred, **3:208**
Binoculars, **3:208-209**, *3:208*
Biochemistry, **3:209-210**, *3:209*
Biodegradability, **3:210**, 16:1475
Biodynamic farming 1:39
Biofeedback, **3:210**
Biogas, **3:210**
Biological clock, **3:210-11**, 3:217, 4:371
Biological control, **3:211**, *3:211*
Biological warfare, **4:346**, *4:346*
Biology, **3:212-13**, *3:212-13*
Bioluminescence, **3:214**, *3:214*
Biomass, **3:214**, *3:214*
Biome, **3:214-15**, *3:215*
Bionics, **3:215**, *3:215,* 5:475
Biophysics, **3:215-17**, *3:216*
Biopsy, 4:297
Biorhythms, 3:217
Biosphere, **3:217**
Biotechnology, **3:217-19**, *3:217-18*
Birch, **3:219**, *3:219, 16:1489*
Bird, *1:91,* **3:220-22**, *3:220-22, 5:465,* 15:1363, 15:1408, *19:1747, 21:2011. See also* specific types.
Bismuth, **3:223**

C

D

E

Eagle, *1:24*, **6:566**, *6:566*, 16:1515

Ear, **6:567-68**, *6:567-68*

Earth, 5:449, **6:569-71**, *6:569-70*, 16:1458, *16:1511*

Earthquake, 5:449, **6:572-74**, *6:572-74*, 7:654, *7:654, 8:691*, 13:1184, 18:1643, 18:1675, 18:1709, 21:1973

Earthworm, *1:92*, **6:575**, *6:575*

Earwig, **6:575-76**, *11:982*

Eastman, George, **6:576**

Ebony, **6:576**, *6:576*

Echidna, **7:581**, *7:581*

Echinoderm. *See* Echinodermata.

Echinodermata, **7:581-82**, *7:582*

Echo, 1:21, **7:582**

Eclipse, **7:582-83**, *7:583*

Ecliptic, **7:583**

Ecology, *3:213*, **7:584**, *7:584*, 7:585, 15:1380

Ecosystem, 7:584, **7:585-88**, *7:585-88*, 11:1034, 20:1861

Ectoplasm, **7:589**

Eczema, **7:589**

Edison, Thomas Alva, **7:589-90**, *7:589*, 7:604

Eel, **7:590**, *7:590, 7:598*

Effervescence, **7:591**

Efficiency, **7:591**

Efflorescence, **7:591**

Egg, **7:592-93**, *7:592-93*, 13:1180, 15:1367, 17:1621, *17:1622, 17:1626*, 19:1804

Eggplant, **7:594**, *7:594*

Egret, *3:221*, **7:594**, *7:594*

Eider, **7:594-95**, *7:595*

Einstein, Albert, **7:595-96**, *7:595*, 17:1561, 17:1617

Eland, **7:596**, *7:596*

Elasticity, **7:596-97**, *7:596*

Elderberry, **7:597**, *7:597*

Electrical engineering, 7:650

Electric bell, **7:597**, *7:597*

Electric fish, **7:598**, *7:598*

Electricity, 5:473, 7:597, 7:598, 7:590, **7:599-603**, *7:599-603*, 7:604, 7:606, 7:650, *15:1437*

Generation, 7:600, 8:767, 9:800

Electric light, *7:589*, 7:590, **7:604-605**, *7:604*, 10:958, *11:966*, 14:1299

Electric locomotive, 12:1103, *17:1589*

Electric motor, 5:421, **7:606-608**, *7:606, 15:1438*

Electrocardiogram (ECG), **7:608**, *7:608*

Electrode, **7:609**

Electroencephalograph (EEG), **7:609**

Electrolysis, **7:609-611**, *7:609-610*

Electromagnet, 7:597, *7:612*, 7:613

Electromagnetic radiation, **7:611**, *7:611*

Electromagnetic spectrum, 7:611, *7:611, 22:2060*

Electromagnetism, **7:612-13**, 11:969

Electromotive force (EMF), **7:614**, *7:614*

Electromotive series, **7:614**

Electron, 2:146-48, **7:615**, 21:1929, 21:1935

Electronic music, **7:615**, *7:615*, 19:1788

Electronics, **7:616-19**, *7:616-19*

Electron microscope, **7:620**, *7:620*, 17:1561

Electrophoresis, **7:621**

Electroplating, *7:609-610*

Electroscope, **7:621**, *7:621*, 7:622

Electrostatics, **7:621-22**, *7:622*

Element, 5:424, 7:623-25, *7:623-25*, 11:1009, 17:1617, 21:1963, 21:1964, 21:1997, 23:2122-23

Elementary particles, **7:626**, 14:1306, 15:1393, 23:2121

Elephant, *5:416*, **7:626-28**, *7:626-27, 20:1897, 22:2110*

Elephant seal, **7:628**, *7:628, 18:1701*

Elk, **7:629**, *7:629, 10:955*

Ellipse, *5:474*, **7:629-30**, *7:629*

Elm, **7:630**, *7:630*

Embryo, *7:593*, **7:631-33**, *7:631-33*, 7:638, *7:638*, 17:1622

Emerald, **7:634**, *7:634*

Emery, 1:9, 5:453, **7:634**

Emotion, **7:634**

Emphysema, **7:634-35**

Emulsion, **7:635**, 15:1377

Enamel, **7:635**, *7:635*, 15:1378

Endangered species, **7:636**, *7:636*, 8:680, 22:2110, 23:2138-39

Endocrine, *1:85*, **7:637**, 9:829, *9:829*, 10:920

Endoplasm, **7:637**

Endorphin, **7:637-38**

Endoscopy, **7:638**, *7:638*

Endoskeleton, 19:1742

Endosperm, **7:638**, *7:638*

Endothermic reaction, **7:638**

Energy, 6:564, **7:639-43**, *7:639-43*, 11:1025, 15:1437, 16:1507, 21:1930, 22:2089

Engine, 2:154, **7:644-46**, *7:644-46*, 14:1269, 18:1656, 19:1804

Engineering, **7:647-50**, *7:647-50*

ENIAC, 5:426

Enkephalin, **7:651**

Entomology, **7:651**, *7:651*

Entropy, **7:651**, 21:1931

Environment, **7:652**, *7:652*

Environmental issues, 7:652, *7:652*, **7:653**, *7:653*

Enzyme, **7:653**, 12:1076

Eocene epoch, **7:654**, *7:654*

Epicenter, **7:654**, *7:654*

Epidemic, **7:654-55**

Epilepsy, **7:655**

F

G

Gagarin, Yuri Alekseyevich, **9:780**

Galápagos Islands, 7:668, **9:780**, *9:780*

Galaxy, *2:138, 3:205, 6:570,* **9:781-83**, *9:781-83,* 10:893, 13:1216, 17:1610, *17:1611,* 21:1990, *21:1992*

Galen, **9:784**

Galena, **9:784**, *11:1048*

Galileo, **9:784**, *9:784*

Gallbladder, **9:785-85**

Gallinule, *22:2040*

Gallstone, 9:785

Gall wasp, **9:785**, *9:785*

Galvani, Luigi, **9:785-86**

Galvanizing, **9:786**, *9:786,* 22:2109, *22:2109*

Galvanometer, **9:786-87**

Gamete, **9:787**, 13:1176, 22:2112

Gamma ray, **9:787**, 17:1570, 17:1582, *20:1904*

Gannet, *8:722*

Gar, **9:787-88**

Garlic, *1:38, 3:264,* **9:788**, *9:788*

Garnet, **9:788**, *9:788*

Garter snake, **9:788**

Gas, **9:789-90**, *9:789-90,* 20:1834, 21:2000

Gasohol, 1:55, 7:641, 9:792, *9:792*

Gasoline, **9:791-92**, 14:1343, *15:1418,* 20:1920

Gasoline engine, 7:644, *7:644-45*

Gastric juice, **9:793**

Gastropod, 1:7, **9:793-94**, *9:793-94*

Gas turbine, 1:50, *1:50,* **9:794-95**, *9:794-95*

Gauss, **9:795**

Gauss, Karl Freidrich, **9:796**

Gazelle, *1:61,* **9:796**, *9:796, 17:1621*

Gear, 2:155, *2:155,* 6:519, **9:797-98**, *9:797*

Gecko, **9:798**, *9:798*

Geiger counter, **9:798-99**, *9:799*

Gem, 7:634, **9:799**, *9:799. See also* Precious stone.

Gender, **9:799**

Gene, 1:63, 4:367, 6:538, 6:543, **9:799**, 9:802, 9:803, 9:807, 10:902, 10:937, 15:1421, 17:1607

Generator, electrical, 6:565, **9:800-801**, *9:801, 21:1979*

Genetic engineering, 3:218, **9:802**, *9:802*

Genetic fingerprinting, 8:745, **9:802**

Genetics, 7:666, **9:803-806**, *9:803, 9:805,* 10:902

Genome project, **9:807**

Genotype, **9:807**

Genus, **9:807**

Geochemistry, **9:807**, *9:807*

Geode, **9:807-808**, *9:808*

Geography, **9:808-809**, *9:808*

Geological map, **9:809**

Geological time scale, **9:809**, 15:1409, 23:2128

Geology, 9:809, **9:810-12**, *9:810-12,* 9:816

Geometry, **9:813-15**, *9:815,* 16:1496, 20:1883, 21:1952, 23:2144

Geomorphology, **9:816**, *9:816*

Geophysics, *9:816*

Geothermal energy, *7:641, 7:642, 8:766*

Geranium, **9:816-17**, *9:817, 11:974*

Gerbil, **9:817**, *9:817, 22:2040*

Germ, **9:817**

Germanium, **9:818**

German measles, **9:818**

Germination, **9:818-19**, *9:818,* 18:1708

Gerontology and geriatrics, **9:819**, *9:819*

Gestation period, **9:820**, *9:820,* 16:1517

Geyser, **19:1817-18**, *19:1817*

Giant panda, *15:1382*

Giant sequoia, **9:820-21**, *9:821, 9:858*

Giant star, **9:821**, *9:821*

Gibberellins, **9:821**

Gibbon, *1:90,* **9:822**, *9:822*

Gila monster, **9:822**, *9:822*

Gilbert, William, **9:822-23**

Gilbreth family, **9:823**

Gills, *8:714,* **9:823-24**, *9:823, 17:1632*

Ginger family, **9:824**, *9:824, 18:1641*

Ginkgo, **9:824**, *9:824*

Ginseng family, *1:37,* **9:824-25**

Giraffe, *1:24,* **9:825**, *9:825, 14:1292*

Glaciation, **9:825-26**, *9:826*

Glacier, 1:34, 6:557, 9:825, **9:827-28**, *9:827-28,* 14:1260

Gladdon, *18:1707*

Gladiolus, **9:828**, *9:828*

Gland, 7:637, **9:828-29**, *9:829,* 10:920

Glass, **9:830-33**, *9:830-33*

Glaucoma, **9:834**

Glenn, John Herschel, **9:834**, *9:834*

Glider, 1:48, *2:163, 5:443*

Global warming, 9:853

Glucose, **9:834-35**, 11:989

Glue, 1:27

Gluten, **9:835**

Gluteus maximus, **9:835**

Gnu, **9:835**, *9:835*

Goat, **9:835-36**, *9:836*

Goddard, Robert Hutchings, **9:836**, 18:1658, *18:1659*

Gold, *7:623,* **9:836-38**, *9:837*

Golden oriole, *16:1500*

Goldenrod, **9:838**, *9:838*

Goldfish, *3:253,* **9:838**, *9:838*

Gonorrhea, **9:838-39**

Goodall, Jane, **9:839-40**, *9:839*

Googol, **9:840**

Goose, **9:840**, *9:840*

L

Lacewing, **11:1031**, *11:1031*
Lacquer, **11:1031-32**, 15:1377
Lactic acid, **11:1032**
Ladybug, *3:197*, **11:1032**, *11:1032*
Lakes, *5:461, 8:735, 9:828*, **11:1033-34**, *11:1033-34*, *20:1874*, 23:2129
Lamarck, Jean Baptiste, 7:666, **11:1035**, *11:1035*
Lamprey, *8:716*, **11:1035-36**, *11:1035*
Landslide, **11:1036**, *11:1036*
Lanthanide, **11:1036-37**
Lapis lazuli, **11:1037**, *11:1037*
Laplace, Pierre Simon, **11:1037**
Laptop computer, *5:430*
Larch, *9:863*, **11:1037-38**, *11:1038, 14:1253, 16:1488*
Lark, **11:1038**, *11:1038*
Larva, 3:269, *3:270*, **11:1038-39**, *11:1038*, 13:1194
Larynx, **11:1039**, *11:1039*, 22:2025
Laser, *4:322*, 10:914-15, *10:915*, 10:916, **11:1040-42**, *11:1040-42*, 17:1569, 21:2015
Latent heat, **11:1043**
Latex, 18:1664, 18:1667
Lathe, **11:1043-44**, *11:1043*
Latitude, **11:1044**, *11:1044*, 14:1294
Laurel, **11:1044,** *11:1044*
Lava, *10:958*, **11:1044-45**, *11:1045*, 22:2028
Lavender, **11:1045**, *11:1045*
Lavoisier, Antoine, **11:1046**, *11:1046*
Lawrence, Ernest, **11:1046**
Laxative, **11:1046-47**
LCD (liquid crystal display), **11:1047-48**, *11:1047*
Leaching, **11:1048**
Lead, **11:1048**, *11:1048*

Leaf, *2:228*, 4:364, *4:367*, **11:1049-51**, *11:1049-51*, 15:1432, 16:1467, 20:1848, *21:1945*
Leaf insect, **11:1052**, *11:1052*
Leakey family, 2:102, **11:1052**, *11:1052*
Learning, **11:1053-54**, *11:1053-54*
Learning disorder, **11:1055**
Leather, 20:1886
LED (light-emitting diode), **11:1055-56**, *11:1056*
Lee, Tsung Dao, **11:1056**, *11:1056*
Leech, *1:92*, **12:1061**, *12:1061*
Leek, *1:38*, **12:1061**, *12:1061*
Leeuwenhoek, Anton Van, **12:1061-62**
Legionnaires' disease, **12:1062**
Legume, **12:1062**, *12:1062*, 15:1398, *22:2072*
Lemming, **12:1062-63**, *12:1063*
Lemon, *3:202, 4:375*
Lemur, **12:1063**, *12:1063, 16:1500*
Lens, 1:8, 3:284, *3:286-87*, 5:431, *5:431*, 5:443, *5:443*, **12:1063-65**, *12:1064*, 12:1081, *12:1131, 15:1356-57*, 16:1529, 20:1903
Lentil, **12:1065**, *12:1065*
Lenz's law, **12:1065**
Leonardo da Vinci, **12:1066**, *12:1066*
Leopard, **12:1066-67**, *12:1066-67*
Leprosy, **12:1067**
Lesseps, Ferdinand De, **12:1067**
Letterpress, *16:1523-24*, 16:1526
Lettuce, *1:38*, **12:1068**, *12:1068, 21:2004*
Leucocyte, 3:229, **12:1068**, *12:1068*
Leukemia, **12:1068-69**
Levee, **12:1069-70**, *12:1069*

Lever, 8:767, **12:1070-71**, *12:1070*, 12:1122, *12:1122*
Leyden jar, **12:1071**
Libby, Willard Frank, **12:1071**
Lice, **12:1071-72**, *12:1071*
Lichen, *7:585*, **12:1072-73**, *12:1072*, 20:1882
Licorice, **12:1073**, *12:1073*
Lie detector, **12:1073**
Life, *7:666*, **12:1074-77**, *12:1075-77*, 18:1711
Life cycle, **12:1078**, *12:1078-79*, 13:1194
Lift, 1:30
Ligament, **12:1079**, *12:1079*, 19:1817
Light, 6:532, 11:1040, **12:1080-82**, *12:1080-82*, 13:1227, 15:1424, 15:1431, 16:1485, 17:1595, 17:1612, 17:1613, 18:1689
Lighthouse, **12:1083**, *12:1083*
Lightning, *7:599*, **12:1083-84**, *12:1084*
Light-year, **12:1084**
Lignin, **12:1084**, *12:1084*
Lignite, **12:1084**, *12:1084*
Lilac, **12:1085**, *12:1085, 18:1728*
Lily family, **12:1085**, *12:1085*
Lime (fruit), *4:375*
Limestone, 4:321, *4:321, 9:816*, **12:1085-86**, *12:1086*, 12:1147, 19:1823
Limpet, **12:1086**, *12:1086, 13:1242*
Linear accelerator, 1:14, *1:14*
Linden, **12:1087**, *12:1087*
Liner, *18:1724*
Linnaeus, Carolus, **12:1087**
Lion, *5:416, 6:538*, **12:1087-88**, *12:1088, 19:1751*
Liquefaction, **12:1088-89**
Liquid, **12:1089-90**, *12:1089-90*, 13:1179, 20:1834, 20:1873, 22:2024, 22:2025
Liquid air, **12:1090**, *12:1090*
Lister, Joseph, **12:1090-91**
Lithium, **12:1091**, *12:1091*

M

N

P

Q

R

Red giant, **17:1610**, *17:1610*, 20:1831

Red shift, **17:1610-11**, *17:1611*

Reducing agent, 15:1369

Reduction, **15:1368-69**

Redwood, **17:1611**, *17:1611*

Reed, **17:1611-12**, *17:1612*

Reed, Walter, **17:1612**

Reef, 5:449, 9:852

Reflection of light, *1:10*, 12:1080, 13:1227, 15:1356, *15:1356*, **17:1612-13**, *17:1613*

Reflex, 15:1397, **17:1613**

Refraction of light, 12:1063, 12:1081, 15:1356, *15:1356*, **17:1613-14**, *17:1614*

Refrigeration, **17:1614-15**, *17:1615*

Regeneration, **17:1615-16**, *17:1616*

Reindeer, *1:91*, **17:1616-17**, *17:1616*

Reinforced materials, **17:1617**

Relative atomic mass, **17:1617**

Relative density, 10:948, **17:1617**

Relative molecular mass, **17:1617**

Relativity, 7:595, 12:1160, **17:1617-18**, *17:1618*

Relay, **17:1619**

REM, **17:1619**

Remora, **17:1619**, *20:1862*

Remote control, **17:1619**

Remote sensing, **17:1619-20**

Reproduction, 3:253, 16:1517, **17:1620-23**, *17:1620-22*

Reproductive System, **17:1623-24**, *17:1624*, 18:1716

Reptile, **17:1625-26**, *17:1625-26, 19:1747, 21:2011. See also* specific types.

Reservoir, **17:1627**, *17:1627, 22:2057*

Resin, 1:23, 7:656, 11:1031, 14:1335, **17:1627-28**, *17:1628*, 18:1721

Resistance, electrical, 5:433, 14:1344, 17:1604, **17:1628**, 21:1933

Resistor, **17:1628-29**

Resonance, **17:1629-30**, *17:1629*

Resource exploitation, **17:1630**, *17:1630*

Respiration, 1:29, 3:249, 11:1030, 12:1116, 15:1371, **17:1631-32**, *17:1631-32*, 18:1637

Respiratory system, **18:1637-38**, *18:1637-38*, 19:1813

Reversible reaction, **18:1639**

Revolution, **18:1639**

Revolver, *9:861*, 9:862

Rhesus factor, **18:1639**

Rheumatic fever, **18:1639**

Rhinoceros, *7:636, 10:954, 16:1479*, **18:1639-40**, *18:1640*

Rhizome, 9:824, **18:1641**, *18:1641*

Rhododendron, *10:890*, **18:1641**, *18:1641*

Rhubarb, *1:38, 16:1484*, **18:1641**, *18:1641*

Rib, **18:1641-42**

Ribosome, **18:1642**

Rice, *1:37*, **18:1642-43**, *18:1642-43*

Richter scale, **18:1643**

Rickets, **18:1643-44**

Rickettsia, **18:1644**, *18:1644*, 21:1983

Rifle, *9:861*

Rift valley, **18:1644-45**, *18:1644*

Right whale, **18:1645**, *18:1645, 22:2077*

Ringworm, **18:1645**

River, 7:661, **18:1646-49**, *18:1646-49*, 23:2129

RNA, 14:1326, **18:1650**

Roadrunner, **18:1650**, *18:1650*

Robin, **18:1650-51**, *18:1651*

Robotics, **18:1651-53**, *18:1652-53, 20:1894*

Rock, *9:811*, 10:957-58, *10:958*, 11:1016, 12:1085, 12:1125, 13:1220, 15:1350, 17:1554, **18:1654-55**, *18:1654*, 18:1677, 18:1691, 18:1706, *20:1851*, 22:2070

Rock cycle, **18:1655**

Rocket, *6:654*, 9:836, 11:1014, 13:1229, *13:1230, 14:1317*, **18:1656-59**, *18:1656-57, 18:1659, 19:1796-1803*

Rock salt, **18:1660**, *18:1660*

Rodent, **18:1660-61**, *18:1660*

Roemer, Olaus, **18:1661**

Roentgen, **18:1661**

Roentgen, Wilhelm Conrad, **18:1661**

ROM, 4:322, 5:429

Roman numerals, 2:120, 23:2144

Root, 16:1466, **18:1662-63**, *18:1662*, 20:1853, 21:1973

Root crop, **18:1663**

Root, mathematical, **18:1663**

Rorqual, **18:1663**

Rose family, *1:89*, **18:1663-64**, *18:1664*

Rosewood, **18:1664**

Rotifer, **18:1664**

Rubber, *12:1125*, **18:1664-67**, *18:1666*, 18:1667, 22:2034

Rubber tree, **18:1667**, *18:1667*

Rubella, 9:818

Rubeola, 13:1168

Ruby, **18:1667-68**, *18:1667*

Rue family, **18:1668**, *18:1668*

Ruminant, **18:1668-69**, *18:1668*

Rush, **18:1669**, *18:1669*

Rust, 5:452, *5:452, 15:1369*, **18:1669**

Rust (plant disease), *16:1463*, **18:1670**, *18:1670*

Rutherford, Ernest, 1:15, 1:68, 14:1328, *14:1328*, 15:1392, **18:1670**

Rutile, **18:1670-71**

Rye, *1:36*, **18:1671**, *18:1671*

Rye grass, 9:848

S

Sabin, Albert Bruce, **18:1671**
Sabin, Florence, **18:1671-72**
Sable, **18:1672**
Sage, *11:1051*
Salamander, 1:78, *1:78*, 14:1275, 14:1307, **18:1672-73**, *18:1672-73*
Salinity, **18:1673**
Saliva, **18:1673**
Salk, Jonas Edward, **18:1673-74**
Salmon, **18:1674**, *18:1674*
Salmonella, *13:1203*, **18:1674-75**
Salt, 6:501. *See also* Sodium chloride.
Saltpeter, **18:1675**
Salts, **18:1675**
Salvia, *11:1051*
San Andreas Fault, **18:1675**
Sand, 6:559, 17:1565, **18:1675-76**, *18:1676, 19:1734*
Sandalwood, **18:1676-77**, *18:1676*
Sand blasting, **18:1677**
Sand dollar, *7:582*, **18:1677**, *18:1677*
Sandstone, **18:1677-78**, *18:1677, 18:1706*
Sap, **18:1678**
Sapphire, *9:799*, **18:1678**, *18:1678*
Saprophyte, **18:1679**, *18:1679*
Sapsucker, **18:1679**, *18:1679*
Sapwood, **18:1679-80**
Sarcodine, 17:1541, *17:1543*
Sardine, **18:1680**
Sargasso, **18:1680**
Sassafras, **18:1680**, *18:1680*
Satellite, *2:135, 13:1199, 14:1295, 15:1359*, **18:1681-83**, *18:1681-83*, 19:1820, 20:1901, *22:2068*
Saturn, 16:1459, *16:1460*, **18:1684-85**, *18:1684-85*
Sawfish, **18:1686**, *18:1686*
Sawfly, **18:1686**

Saxifrage family, **18:1686**, *18:1686*
Scale, **18:1687**
Scale insect, **18:1687**, *18:1687*
Scallop, **18:1687-88**, *18:1687*
Scanning tunneling microscope, **18:1688**
Scarab, *3:197*, **18:1688-89**, *18:1688*
Scarlatina. *See* Scarlet fever.
Scarlet fever, **18:1689**
Scarp, **18:1689**, *18:1689*
Scattering, **18:1689-90**
Scavenger, **18:1690**, *18:1690*
Scheele, Carl Wilhelm, **18:1690**
Schist, **18:1691**, *18:1691*
Schistosomiasis, **18:1691**
Schrodinger, Erwin, **18:1691**
Schwann, Theodor, **18:1691**
Science, **18:1692-95**, *18:1692-94. See also* individual sciences.
Sclerenchyma, **18:1696**
Scorpion, *2:114*, **18:1696**, *18:1696*
Scorpion fly, **18:1696-97**
Screw, **18:1697**, *18:1697*
Scurvy, **18:1698**
Sea, 6:501, **18:1698**, 23:2129
Sea anemone, *5:397*, **18:1698**, *18:1698*
Seaborg, Glenn Theodore, **18:1698-99**
Sea cow, 12:1139, *12:1139*
Sea cucumber, *7:582*, **18:1699**, *18:1699*
Sea horse, **18:1699-1700**, *18:1699*
Seal, **18:1700-1701**, *18:1700-1701*
Sealab, **18:1701**
Sea lavender, *10:877*
Sea lion, **18:1702**, *18:1702*
Sea slug, *9:794*, **18:1702**, *18:1702*
Sea snake, **18:1702**, *18:1702*
Season, **18:1703**, *18:1703*, 19:1781
Sea squirt, **18:1704**, *18:1704*

Sea urchin, *7:582*, 18:1677, *18:1677*, **18:1704**
Seawater, 6:501
Seaweed, *1:57, 1:58, 11:999, 16:1469*, **18:1704-1705**, *18:1705*
Sebaceous gland, 1:20
Secondary battery, 2:183
Sedative, **18:1705**
Sedge family, **18:1705-1706**, *18:1706*
Sedimentary rock, 18:1655, **18:1706**, *18:1706*
Seed, 6:533, 7:638, *7:638*, 9:818, *9:818*, **18:1707-1708**, *18:1707-1708*, 18:1717, *18:1717*
Seismology, *6:574*, 18:1643, **18:1709**
Seizure, 7:655
Selective breeding, **18:1709**
Self-pollination, **18:1709**
Semicircular canal, *6:568*
Semiconductor, 4:360, 5:434, 9:818, 15:1425, **18:1710-11**, *18:1710, 19:1735*, 19:1772, 21:1929, 21:1961
Semipermeable membrane, 15:1364
Senecio, *21:1968*
Sense, **18:1711**
Sensitivity, **18:1711**
Sensor, **18:1711-12**
Sepal, **18:1712**, *18:1712*
Separation, **18:1712-13**, *18:1712*
Serpentine, **18:1713**
Serum, **18:1713**
Serval, **18:1713-14**, *18:1714*
Set theory, **18:1714-15**, *18:1714-15*
Sewage treatment, **18:1715-16**
Sex, 9:799, 17:1624, **18:1716**, 20:1846, 22:2100, 22:2104
Sex chromosomes, **18:1716**
Sextant, *14:1293*, 14:1294
Sexually transmitted disease, 9:839, **18:1717**, 20:1885

T

Talc, **20:1885**
Tanager, **20:1886**, *20:1886*
Tangent, 21:1970
Tanning, **20:1886**, *20:1886*
Tape recorder, 19:1790
Tapeworm, **20:1887**, *20:1887*
Tapir, **20:1887-88**, *20:1887*
Tarantula, **20:1888**, *20:1888*
Tarpon, **20:1888**
Tarsal, **20:1888-89**
Tarsier, **20:1889**
Tartar, **20:1889**
Tartaric acid, **20:1889**
Tasmanian devil, *13:1158*,
    20:1889, *20:1889*
Tasmanian wolf, **20:1889**
Taste, 14:1319, **20:1890-91**,
    20:1890
Tautomerism, *11:1008*, 11:1009
Taxidermy, **20:1892**
Taxonomy, **20:1892**
T Cell, 1:40, *1:41*
Tea, **20:1892-93**, *20:1892-93*
Teak, **20:1893**, *20:1893*
Technology, **20:1894**, *20:1894*
Teeth, 4:308, 6:498-99,
    20:1889, **20:1895-97**,
    20:1895-97
Teflon, 16:1498
Telecommunication, 17:1571-
    75, 18:1682, **20:1898**,
    20:1898
Telegraph, 5:419, 14:1262,
    20:1898-99
Telemetry, **20:1899**, *20:1899*
Telephone, 3:200, 5:419-20,
    13:1238, 17:1571, *17:1571*,
    20:1900-1902, *20:1900-
    1902*
Telescope, 2:136-37, *2:136-37*,
    14:1338, **20:1903-1906**,
    20:1903-1906
Television, 3:288, *4:318*,
    10:957, **20:1907-1911**,
    20:1907-1910
Teller, Edward, **20:1912**

Temperature, 8:688, 17:1558,
    19:1824, **20:1912**, 21:1932,
    21:1934, 22:2067
Temperature, body, 10:952,
    20:1912-13, *20:1912*
Tendon, **20:1913**
Tendril, **20:1913**, *20:1913*
Tension, **20:1913-14**
Terminal velocity, **20:1914**
Termite, *18:1690*, **20:1914-15**,
    20:1914-15
Tern, **20:1915-16**, *20:1916*
Terrapin, **20:1916**, *20:1916*
Territory, **20:1916-17**
Tertiary period, **20:1917**
Tesla, Nikola, **20:1917-20**,
    20:1917-19
Testicle, **20:1920**
Test tube baby, **20:1920**
Tetanus, **20:1920**
Tetraethyl lead, **20:1920**
Textile, *11:971*, **21:1925-28**,
    21:1925-28
Thallus, **21:1929**
Thermal, *10:889*
Thermionic emission, **21:1929**,
    21:1929
Thermistor, **21:1929**, *21:1929*
Thermocouple, 17:1558,
    21:1929-30, *21:1930*
Thermodynamics, 15:1411,
    21:1930-31
Thermography, **21:1931**,
    21:1931
Thermometer, 21:1929,
    21:1932-33, *21:1932-33*
Thermoplastic, 16:1472
Thermoset, 16:1472
Thermostat, **21:1934**, *21:1934*
Thistle, **21:1934-35**, *21:1934*
Thomson, Sir Joseph John,
    21:1935
Thorax, **21:1935**, *21:1935*
Thorn, **21:1935-36,** *21:1936*
Thrasher, **21:1936**
Thrips, **21:1936**
Throat, 11:1039
Thrush, **21:1936**, *21:1936*
Thrust, 1:32, **21:1937**, *21:1937*

Thunderstorm, 12:1083,
    20:1850, **21:1937-38**,
    21:1938, 21:1953
Thyroid gland, 10:921
Tibia, **21:1938**, *21:1938*
Tick, **21:1938-39**, *21:1939*
Tide, 14:1296, **21:1939-40**,
    21:1939
Tiger, *4:309*, **21:1940**, *21:1940*,
    21:1951
Tigerfish, *8:716*
Time, **21:1941**, *21:1941*
Time zone, 19:1824, **21:1942**,
    21:1942
Tin, **21:1942-43**, *21:1943*
Tissue, **21:1944-45**, *21:1944-
    45*
Tissue culture, *3:251*
Titanium, 18:1670, **21:1946**,
    21:1946
Titmouse, **21:1946**, *21:1946*
Titration, **21:1947**, 21:1947
TNT (trinitrotoluene), **21:1947**
Toad, 1:78-79, *1:79*, **21:1947-
    48**, *21:1948*
Tobacco, 19:1758, **21:1948-49**,
    21:1949
Toluene, **21:1949**
Tomato, *1:38, 3:202, 8:739,
    8:760*, **21:1949-50**, *21:1950*
Tombaugh, Clyde William,
    21:1950
Tomography, **21:1950**
Tongue, 20:1890, **21:1950-51**,
    21:1952
Tonsil, **21:1951**
Topaz, **21:1951**, *21:1951*
Topology, **21:1952**, *21:1952*
Tornado, **21:1953**, *21:1953*
Torque, **21:1953-54**, *21:1953*
Torricelli, Evangelista, **21:1954**
Torsion, **21:1954-55**, *21:1954*
Tortoise, *10:909*, **21:1955**,
    21:1955
Toucan, *3:222*, **21:1955-56**,
    21:1956
Touch, **21:1956**
Tourmaline, **21:1956-57**
Toxic waste, **21:1957**, *21:1957*

U

V

Vaccination, *11:973*, 11:1013, 18:1671, 18:1673, 18:1713, 19:1756, **21:1996**, *21:1996*

Vacuole, **21:1996**

Vacuum, **21:1996-97**

Vacuum forming, *16:1473*

Vacuum tube, 7:616, *7:616*, 7:618, *21:1929*, **21:1997**, *21:1997*

Valence, 3:236, 11:1001, **21:1997-98**

Valve. *See* Vacuum tube.

Vampire bat, **21:1998**, *21:1998*

Van Allen, James Alfred, **21:1998-99**

Van Allen belts, **21:1999**, *21:1999*

Van De Graaff generator, **21:1999-2000**, 21:2000

Van Der Waals, Johannes, **21:2000**

Van Der Waals forces, **21:2000**

Vapor, **21:2000**

Vapor pressure, **21:2000**

Variable star, 20:1830, **21:2000-2001**, *21:2001*

Variation, **21:2001**

Variola, 19:1756

Varnish, **21:2001**

Vascular plant, 16:1466, **21:2002-2003**, *21:2002*

Vector quantity, **21:2003**

Vegetable, **21:2003-2004**, *21:2004. See also* specific types.

Vegetative propagation, **21:2005-2006**, *21:2005*

Vein, *4:373*, 4:374, 10:884-85, 15:1422, **21:2006**

Velocity, 1:13, **21:2006**

Vena cava, **21:2006-2007**

Venom, 19:1761

Vent, **21:2007**, *21:2007*

Ventricle, 10:884, **21:2007**

Venus, 16:1458, **21:2008-2009**, *21:2008-2009*

Venus's-flytrap, *1:89, 4:309*, **21:2010**, *21:2010*

Vertebra, 19:1755, **21:2010**, *21:2010*

Vertebrate, **21:2010-11**, *21:2011*

Vestigial organ, **21:2011**

Vetch, *15:1398*, **21:2011-12**, *21:2011*

Veterinary medicine, **21:2012**, *21:2012*

Viburnum, *18:1728*, **21:2012**, *21:2012*

Video recording, *17:1607*, 20:1911, **21:2013-15**, *21:2013-15*

Villi, **21:2016**

Vine family, **21:2016**

Vinyl, **21:2016**

Violets, **21:2016**, *21:2016*

Viper, 1:26, *19:1760*, **22:2021**, *22:2021*

Viperfish, *1:12*

Vireo, **22:2021**, *22:2021*

Virginia creeper, *4:384*, **22:2021**

Virus, 5:405, 6:531, 10:906, 11:975, *11:975*, 14:1277, *16:1463*, 17:1567, **22:2021-23**, *22:2021-22*, 22:2107

Virus, computer, **22:2023**, *22:2023*

Viscosity, **22:2924**

Vision. *See* Eye and vision.

Vitamin, 3:201, 6:494, 6:515, 14:1333, 18:1642, 18:1643, 18:1698, **22:2024-25**, *22:2024*, 23:2141

Voice, **22:2025**, *22:2025*

Volatile liquid, **22:2025**

Volcano, 3:277, *5:441, 9:812*, 11:1044, 14:1271, 21:2007, *21:2007*, **22:2026-31**, *22:2026-31*

Vole, **22:2032**, *22:2032*

Volt, 14:1344, 16:1507, **22:2032**, 22:2033

Volta, Alessandro, **22:2032**

Voltage regulator, **22:2033**

Voltmeter, *7:614*, **22:2033**, *22:2033*

Volume, **22:2033**

Volumetric analysis, 4:345, 21:1947

Volvox, **22:2033-34**, *22:2033*

VTOL, 1:49

Vulcanization, 18:1665, *18:1666*, **22:2034**, *22:2034*

Vulture, **22:2035**, *22:2035*

W

Wader, **22:2036**, *22:2036*

Waksman, Selman Abraham, **22:2036**

Walkingstick (stick insect), *4:293*, **22:2036-37**, *22:2037*

Wallaby, *13:1157-58*, **22:2037**, *22:2037*

Wallace, Alfred Russel, **22:2037-38**

Walleye, **22:2038**

Wallflower, **22:2038**, *22:2038*

Walnut, **22:2038-39**, *22:2038*

Walrus, **22:2039**, *22:2039*

Wankel engine, *7:646*, *7:646*

Warbler, **22:2039-40**, *22:2039*

Warm-blooded animal, **22:2040-41**, *22:2040-41*

Warm front, *8:758*, **22:2041**

Warning coloration, **22:2041-42**, *22:2042*

Wart hog, **22:2042**

Wasp, *9:785*, *9:785*, *10:923*, *16:1516*, **22:2042-43**, *22:2043*

Waste disposal, *3:218*, *16:1475*, *17:1579*, *17:1579*, *18:1715-16*, *21:1957*, **22:2044-47**, *22:2044-47*

Watch, **5:389-92**, *5:389*

Water, *9:855*, *10:947*, *11:1006*, **22:2048-52**, *22:2048-52*, 22:2053, 22:2056, 22:2058

Watercress, *16:1464*, **22:2053**

Water cycle, **22:2053-54**, *22:2053*

Waterfall, *20:1919*, **22:2054-55**, *22:2054*

Water flea, **22:2055**, *22:2055*

Water lily, *2:112*, *11:1051*, **22:2055-56**, *22:2055*

Watershed, **22:2056**

Water softening, **22:2056**

Water supply, 2:124, 22:2052, **22:2056-58**, *22:2057*

Water table, **22:2058**

Watson, James Dewey, **22:2058-59**, *22:2058*

Watt, **22:2059**

Watt, James, *20:1840*, **22:2059**, *22:2059*

Wave, *6:520*, *6:520*, *7:642*, 11:991, *11:991*, 11:1040, 12:1080, 14:1339, 15:1431, 17:1572, 19:1784, 19:1824, **22:2060-62**, *22:2060-62*

Wax, **22:2063**, *22:2063*

Waxwing, *6:534*, **22:2063**, *22:2063*

Weak nuclear force, **22:2063-64**, *22:2064*

Weasel, 13:1159, **22:2064**, *22:2064*

Weather, 1:47, *4:379*, *8:758*, 13:1197-99, 18:1703, **22:2065-69**, *22:2065-69*, 22:2086

Weathering, 22:2070, *22:2070*

Weber, **22:2070**

Webworm, **22:2070-71**, *22:2071*

Weed, *10:900*, **22:2071-73**, *22:2071-72*

Weevil, *3:197*, *3:235*, *16:1516*, **22:2073**, *22:2073*

Weight, *9:851*, 13:1160, **22:2073**

Weightlessness, **22:2074**, *22:2074*

Welding, *13:1189*, **22:2075**, *22:2075*

Well, **22:2075-76**, *22:2076*

Wertheimer, Max, 17:1546, **22:2076**

Whale, *3:199*, 3:233, *3:233*, 12:1138, 14:1287, 16:1504, *18:1645*, 18:1663, *19:1809*, **22:2077-80**, *22:2077-80*

Wheat, *1:36*, *11:968*, 22:2072, 22:2081, *22:2081*

Wheel, **22:2082**, *22:2082*

Wheelbarrow, *12:1121*

Whelk, *13:1242*

Whippoorwill, **22:2082-83**

Whirligig, **22:2083**, *22:2083*

White dwarf, 20:1831, **22:2083**

Whitefish, **22:2083**

Whitney, Eli, **22:2083-84**

Whittle, Sir Frank, **22:2084**

Wiener, Norbert, **22:2084**

Wildebeest, *13:1214*. See also Gnu.

Williams, Daniel Hale, **22:2084**

Willow family, **22:2084-85**, *22:2085*

Wilting, **22:2085**

Wind, *1:43*, 2:187, 14:1255, **22:2086-89**, *22:2086-89*

Wind-chill factor, 23:2144

Windmill, *7:643*, 22:2089

Windpipe. See Trachea.

Wind tunnel, 1:32, *1:32*

Wing, **22:2090**, *22:2090*

Wire, **22:2090-91**, *22:2091*

Wisteria, **22:2091**, *22:2091*

Witch hazel family, **22:2092**, *22:2092*

Wolf, **22:2092-93**, *22:2093*

Wolverine, **22:2093**, *22:2093*

Womb. See Uterus.

Wombat, *13:1158*, **22:2094**, *22:2094*

Wood, **22:2094-95**, *22:2094*

Woodland, *7:588*

Wood louse, **22:2095**, *22:2095*

Woodpecker, **22:2095-96**, *22:2095*

Woods, Granville T., **22:2096**

Woody plant, **22:2096**, *22:2096*

Wool, *8:700*, 18:1719, 21:1925, **22:2096-97**, *22:2097*

Woolly monkey, *13:1247*

Work, **22:2097**

Worm, *6:575*, *6:575*, 12:1061, 12:1111, 14:1298, *14:1299*, 15:1389, **22:2098**, *22:2098*

Wren, *5:470*, **22:2098**, *22:2098*

Wright Brothers, **22:2098-99**, *22:2099*

Wrought iron, **22:2099-2100**

Wu, Chien-Shiung, **22:2100**

X

X chromosome, 18:1716,
22:2100-2101, *22:2100*
Xanthophyll, **22:2101**
Xerography, **22:2101-2102**,
22:2101
Xerophyte, **22:2102-2103**,
22:2102
X ray, 1:88, 3:226, 3:242,
5:424, *6:499*, 7:618,
13:1171, *13:1173, 15:1375,*
17:1570, 17:1582-83,
17:1584, *17:1584*, 18:1661,
20:1846, *20:1904*, 21:1950,
22:2103-2104, 22:2103
Xylem, 3:281-82, *3:282,*
21:1965, 21:1967, 21:2002,
22:2104, *22:2104*

Y

Y chromosome, 18:1716,
22:2104-2105
Yak, **22:2105**, *22:2105*
Yam, **22:2105**, *22:2105*
Yang, Chen Ning, **22:2105-
2106**
Year, **22:2106**
Yeast, 9:776, **22:2106-2107**,
22:2106
Yellow fever, 8:707-708,
14:1264, **22:2107**
Yew, *16:1484*, **22:2107-2108**,
22:2107
Yucca, **22:2107-2108**

Z

Zebra, *3:199, 10:901, 17:1621,*
22:2108, *22:2108*
Zebu, *11:985*
Zenith, **22:2109**
Zinc, 3:247, 9:786, **22:2109**,
22:2109
Zinc blende, 22:2109
Zodiac, **22:2109-2110**,
22:2110
Zoo, **22:2110-12**, *22:2110-12*
Zoology, **22:2112**
Zygote, 9:787, **22:2112**,
22:2112

ACKNOWLEDGMENTS

Page positions for illustrations are as follows: (t) = top, (b) = bottom, (l) = left, (r) = right, (c) = center.

VOLUME 1

7 (l) J.S. Library International; (r) Heather Angel/Biofotos 9 Black & Decker 10 Andromeda Oxford Limited 11 Life File/Lionel Moss 13 NASA/ESA 14 Atomic Energy Authority Technology 15 CERN Photo 16 CERN Photo 18 J.S. Library International 20 Greenpeace/Zindler 21 Robert Harding Picture Library 22 Mordannt Short Limited 24 Heather Angel/Biofotos 25 (l) Andromeda Oxford Limited; (r) Hutchison Library/Christina Dodwell 26 Heather Angel/Biofotos 28 American Airlines 32 (l) Robert Harding Picture Library; (r) British Aerospace Defence Limited 33 Andromeda Oxford Limited 35 (t) Paul Fuqua; (b) Andromeda Oxford Limited 36 U.S. Department of Agriculture 37 U.S. Department of Agriculture 38 Andromeda Oxford Limited 39 (t) Robert Harding Picture Library/Adam Woolfitt; (b) Paul Fuqua 40 Paul Fuqua 41 (both) National Institutes of Health 42-3 Life File/Mike Maidment 44 Life File/Pendragon 44-5 Life File/Sue Wheat 45 J.S. Library International 48 Aviat Inc. 49 British Aerospace 51 (both) Boeing 52 American Airlines 54 Biofotos/G. Kinns 56 (l) Heather Angel/Biofotos; (r) Oxford Scientific Films/David Thompson 57 Heather Angel/Biofotos 63 Heather Angel/Biofotos 66 (t) Andromeda Oxford Limited; (b) Paul Fuqua 67 (c) Andromeda Oxford Limited; (b) Life File/Emma Lee 69 Smiths Industries Aerospace 70 Alcan 72 Heather Angel/Biofotos 73 Andromeda Oxford Limited 74 Paul Fuqua 76 Heather Angel/Biofotos 80 Oxford Scientific Films/Partridge Dods 86 Science Photo Library/U.S. Department. of Energy 87 Andromeda Oxford Limited 89 (tl/r) Andromeda Oxford Limited; (cl) Graham Bateman; (cr) Andromeda Oxford Limited 93 (both) Andromeda Oxford Limited 94 Oxford Scientific Films/J.A.L. Cooke 95 Heather Angel/Biofotos 96 Paul Fuqua

VOLUME 2

101 Andromeda Oxford Limited 104 Paul Fuqua 107 Life File/Andrew Ward 108 Paul Fuqua 110 (t) NASA 111(t) Heather Angel/ Biofotos; (b) Paul Fuqua 112 Andromeda Oxford Limited 114 (t/cr) Morton Aboretum/John Kohout; (cl) Heather Angel/Biofotos; (cc) Life File/Andy Teare; (b) Heather Angel/Biofotos 115 (t) Heather Angel/Biofotos (b) Ted Kinsey 117 Paul Fuqua 122 NASA 126 Andromeda Oxford Limited 128 TRIP 129 (t) Andromeda Oxford Limited; (b) Heather Angel/Biofotos 130 CAMAS Assoc. Asphalt 131 (t) Heather Angel/Biofotos; (b) Andromeda Oxford Limited 136-7 Science Photo Library/Royal Greenwich Observatory 136 Science Photo Library/Philippe Plailly 137 Science Photo Library/Roger Rossmeyer, Starlight 138-9 Science Photo Library/Roger Rossmeyer, Starlight 139 Science Photo Library/Roger Rossmeyer, Starlight 141 Derek Hall 144 Life File/Chris Jones 149 Science Photo Library/Patrica Loiez, CERN 154 (both) General Motors 155 General Motors 158 Courtesy of Chrysler Corporation 159 Paul Fuqua 160 National Park Service 163 Stephen R. Brown 164 Andromeda Oxford Limited 171 (both) Goodyear Tire & Rubber Co. 173 (tc/tr) Life File/Richard Powers; (b) Andromeda Oxford Limited 174 Jenny Fry 175 (both) Heather Angel 177 Graham Bateman 179 Oxford Scientific Films/Fred Bavendam 180 Library of Congress 181 Heather Angel 183 Ever Ready 184 Alcan 185 Heather Angel 187 NTN Bearings 188 Heather Angel 189 Oxford Scientific Films/D.H. Thompson 190 (l) Heather Angel; (r) Oxford Scientific Films/D.H. Thompson 191 J.S. Library International 192 Graham Bateman

VOLUME 3

197 Andromeda Oxford Limited 198-9 Heather Angel 199 J.S. Library International 200 Heather Angel 201 Life File/Angela Maynard 203 Oxford

VOLUME 5

389 (t) Paul Fuqua; (b) Milwaukee Oxford Chemical Design   392 (both) Andromeda Oxford Limited   395 (l) Andromeda Oxford Limited   398 Andromeda Oxford Limited   399 (both) Andromeda Oxford Limited   403 Andromeda Oxford Limited   404 Coffee Council   409 Andromeda Oxford Limited   410 Andromeda Oxford Limited   412 Macbeth   415 Oxford Scientific Films/G.I. Bernard   416 (t) J.S. Library International; (b) Life File/Flora Torrance   417 Oxford Scientific Films/G.I. Bernard   419 Stephen R. Brown   420 Maxon Europe Limited   421 Science Photo Library/Adrienne Hart-Davis   422 Andromeda Oxford Limited   425 Intergraph   426 Science Photo Library/Ken Eward   427 (tr) Paul Fuqua; (cr) Life File/David Kampfner   429 TRIP/Helene Rogers   430 TRIP/Helene Rogers   431 (l) Andromeda Oxford Limited   439 Nature Photographers/Alan Mitchell   436 M. Chinery   436-7 Life File/Flora Torrance   441 Biofotos/Soames Summerhays   444 TRIP/Bob Turner   445 Andromeda Oxford Limited   446 Image Select   447 Paul Fuqua   448 Oxford Scientific Films/Peter Parks   451 NASA   452 Andromeda Oxford Limited   453 Andromeda Oxford Limited   455 (all) National Cotton Council   457 Oxford Scientific Films/David Shale   460 Bovis Construction   461 (l) Oxford Scientific Films/G.I. Bernard; (r) Oregon Department of Tourism   463 (t) M. Chinery; (b) Paul Fuqua   464 Life File/Emma Lee   466 (cl) Oxford Scientific Films/Michael Leach; (bl) Biofotos/Brian Rogers; (br) Andromeda Oxford Limited   467 Oxford Scientific Films/Steve Early   468 Science Photo Library/Peter Menzel   469 Paul Fuqua   471 Mary Evans Picture Library   472 (c) J.S. Library International; (b) Andromeda Oxford Limited   475 Life File/Flora Torrance   476 Andromeda Oxford Limited   478 Andromeda Oxford Limited   480 Andromeda Oxford Limited

VOLUME 6

485 (cl) Andromeda Oxford Limited; (b) U.S. Department of Energy   487 (bc) Andromeda Oxford Limited; (br) Biofotos/Heather Angel; (bl) Julia Roles   491 (both) Paul Fuqua   492 Science Photo Library/Dr. Morley Read   493 (t) Paul Fuqua; (c) Biofotos/Heather Angel; (b) Andromeda Oxford Limited   495 Oxford Scientific Films/David Thompson   496 Science Photo Library/NASA   498 Science Photo Library/John Greim   499 (t) Science Photo Library/BSIPI Barelle; (c) Courtesy 3M Corporation   502 TRIP   504 Julia Roles   505 Jencons   506 Life File/Wayne Shakell   507 Paul Fuqua   509 De Beers Consolidated Mines   510 (both) De Beers Consolidated Mines   511 (both) De Beers Consolidated Mines   512 Andromeda Oxford Limited   513 Obscura   522 Biofotos/C.A. Henley   524 Paul Fuqua   532 Andromeda Oxford Limited   533 (l) Andromeda Oxford Limited   534 (l) Nature Photographers/Roger Tidman; (r) Oxford Scientific Films/Animals, Animals/Breck P. Kent   536 U.S. Navy   538 Life File/Nigel Wicking   542 (cl) Nature Photographers/Paul Sterry; (br) Nature Photographers/S.C. Bisserot   544 J.S. Library International/I. Link   545 (both) Paul Fuqua   546 Premaphotos Wildlife/K.G. Preston-Mafham   547 Premaphotos Wildlife/K.G. Preston-Mafham   549 Oxford Scientific Films/Martyn Chillmaid   550 Andromeda Oxford Limited   551 (b) Life File/Dave Thompson   552 Ted Horowitz Courtesy Schering Plough   553 (both) Zeneca Corporate Slidebank   554 TRIP   555 Nature Photographers/Brinsley Burbidge   557 Oxford Scientific Films/T.C. Middleton   559 (both) Andromeda Oxford Limited   561 The Colour Museum   562 Science Photo Library/Guy Gillette   563 Paul Fuqua   564 J.S. Library International   570 Science Photo Library/J. Baum & N. Henbest   573 Science Photo Library/U.S. Geological Survey   574 Oxford Scientific Films/Warren Faidley   576 Oxford Scientific Films/David Cayless

VOLUME 7

581 Biofotos/L.A. Henley   583 TRIP/NASA   584 TRIP   585 (c) Life File/Nigel Sitwell; (b) Premaphotos Wildlife/K.G. Preston-Mafham   588 Nature Photographers/Paul Sterry   589 Library of Congress   592 Nature Photographers   595 AIP (Andromeda Oxford Limited)/Niels Bohr Library   596 Andromeda Oxford Limited   597 Premaphotos Wildlife/K.G. Preston-Mafham   599 Science Photo Library/Nelson Medina   602 (t) Paul Fuqua; (b) TVA   603 (both) Paul Fuqua   605 Life File/Andrew Ward

607 Paul Fuqua   608 TRIP   609 TRIP   612 Paul Fuqua   615 International Business Machines Corporation   617 U.K. Electronics Limited/ Andromeda Oxford Limited   619 Ravotnon   620 (t) Science Photo Library/David Scharf; (b) Science Photo Library/Lawrence Migdale   622 Paul Fuqua   623 Paul Fuqua   625 Nature Photographers/E.A. James   626 Premaphotos/K.G. Preston-Mafham   628 Nature Photographers/D. Osborn   629 Biofotos/ Heather Angel   630 Life File/Wayne Shakell   631 Paul Fuqua   634 J.S. Library International   635 TRIP   636 (c) B. Mathew; (b) Nature Photographers/ Paul Sterry   638 Science Photo Library/John Greim 639 TVA/Paul Fuqua   640-1 Life File/Graham Burns 641 Biofotos/Heather Angel   642 Biofotos/Heather Angel   642-3 Biofotos/Geoff Moon   643 Biofotos/ Heather Angel   645 General Motors   646 Cosworth Engineering   647 Eurotunnel   648 British Aerospace Defence Limited   648-9 Science Photo Library/ Novosti Press Agency   650 Baxter Healthcare Inc. 651 Oxford Scientific Films/Chris Sharp   652 J.B. Free   653 J.S. Library International/Steve Martin   655 D. Harris   657 Andromeda Oxford Limited   659 (c) Life File/Julia Highet; (b) Paul Fuqua   662 Life File/Emma Lee   663 (l) Nature Photographers/ Andrew Cleave; (r) Nature Photographers/Robin Bush 664 (l) Premaphotos/K.G. Preston-Mafham; (r) Nature Photographers/Paul Sterry   667 Paul Fuqua   668 TRIP/ Helene Rogers   669 Paul Fuqua   672 Paul Fuqua

VOLUME 8

678 J.S. Library International   679 Andromeda Oxford Limited   682 DSM Engineering Plastic Products U.K. Limited   683 Premaphotos Wildlife/K.G. Preston-Mafham   685 Premaphotos Wildlife/K.G. Preston-Mafham   687 Life File/Mike Evans   688 TRIP/Helene Rogers   689 Paul Fuqua 690 Library of Congress   691 U.S. Geological Survey 692 Nature Photographers/Paul Sterry   693 Biofotos/ Heather Angel   694 Paul Fuqua   695 Wisconsin Milk Marketing Board   696 Spectrum Colour Library   697 (t) Andromeda Oxford Limited; (c) Life File/Angela Maynard   698 (both) Kathleen Bober   699 Paul Fuqua   700 Nature Photographers/Jean Hall   701 (all) Biofotos/Heather Angel   702 Paul Fuqua   703 Derek Hall   704 Mercury Communications Limited

705 TRIP/Helene Rogers   706 (c) Vokes Liquid Filtration; (cr) Andromeda Oxford Limited; (br) Vokes Liquid Filtration   708 (tr) Nature Photographers/ Andrew Cleare; (inset) Biofotos/Heather Angel   709 District of Columbia Fire Department   712 Notifier 713 American Red Cross   715 Nature Photographers/ Paul Sterry   718 Nature Photographers/D.F.E. Russell 720 Nature Photographers/Nicholas Brown   723 (t & cl) Paul Fuqua; (br) Biofotos/Heather Angel   724-5 Paul Fuqua   725 Andromeda Oxford Limited   726 (all) Andromeda Oxford Limited   727 TRIP/ B. Turner   728 Courtesy Fermilab   729 Premaphotos Wildlife/R.A Preston-Mafham   732 (l) Life File/Fraser Ralston; (r) Paul Fuqua   733 Paul Fuqua   734 TRIP/B. Turner   737 Wisconsin Milk Marketing Board   738 Science Photo Library/Pasta Co./James Holmes   738-9 Science Photo Library/Peter Menzel 740 Farmer Giles Foods/Science Photo Library/James Holmes   740-1 Life File/Jan Suttle   742 (t) Life File/ Mike Evans; (b) TRIP/H. Rogers   744 Library of Congress   745 Science Photo Library/Peter Menzel 747 Andromeda Oxford Limited/Eric Crichton   750 Science Photo Library/Tony Craddock   752 (t) Premaphotos Wildlife/K.G. Preston-Mafham; (b) Andromeda Oxford Limited   755 Biofotos/Heather Angel   758 (l) Nature Photographers/E.A. James; (r) TRIP/H. Rogers   759 (both) Biofotos/Heather Angel 761 (cl) Nature Photographers/Brinsley Burbidge (cr) Premaphotos Wildlife/K.G. Preston-Mafham; (br)Life File/Emma Lee   762 Andromeda Oxford Limited 763 The Exxon Corporation   765 Life File/David Heath   766 Life File/Cliff Thradgold   768 Paul Fuqua

VOLUME 9

773 Life File/Lionel Moss   774-5 Andromeda Oxford Limited   775 (both) Andromeda Oxford Limited 776 Life File/David Heath   777 American Iron & Steel Institute   778 Science Photo Library/U.S. Department of Energy   779 Lawrence Livermore Labs 780 Nature Photographers/Paul Sterry   781 TRIP 782 NASA   784 Library of Congress   785 (both) Premaphotos Wildlife/K.G. Preston-Mafham   786 (both) Galvanisers Association   788 (l) Life File/Andrew Ward; (r) Science Photo Library/Roberto de Gugliemo   789 Science Photo Library/David Taylor   790 Science Photo Library/Andrew

McClenaghan 791 The Exxon Corporation 792 Paul Fuqua 794 (l) Biofotos/S. Summerhays; (r) U.S. Air Force 796 Premaphotos Wildlife/K.G. Preston-Mafham 798 Premaphotos Wildlife/K.G. Preston-Mafham 800 TVA/Paul Fuqua 802 (l) Evrelios/Science Photo Library/P. Plailly; (r) Science Photo Library/G. Tompkinson 803 Life File/R. Gregory 807 Thomson Laboratories/Science Photo Library/J. Holmes 808 (t) Paul Fuqua; (b) Life File/W. Shakell 811 (t) Life File/L. Moss; (c) Life File/L. Oldroyd 812 Starlight/ Science Photo Library/R. Ressmeyer 815 Paul Fuqua 816 Biofotos/Heather Angel 817 Andromeda Oxford Limited 819 Science Photo Library/W. and D. Mcintyre 821 Courtesy State of California Department of Forestry 822 Nature Photographers Ltd/S. C. Bisserot 823 Biofotos/Heather Angel 824 (l) Life File/Jeremy Hoare; (r) Nature Photographers Limited/A. Cleave 825 Premaphotos Wildlife/K.G. Preston-Mafham 826 Life File/W. Shakell 828 (t) Life File/Andrew Ward; (b) Andromeda Oxford Limited 831 (l) Bristol Blue Glass Limited; (r) Courtesy of Corning Limited, ISPD Europe (QVF Process Systems Limited) 832 Life File/Emma Lee 833 Biofotos/Heather Angel 834 NASA 836 Paul Fuqua 837 (l) Life File/Flor Torrance; (r) TRIP/H. Rogers 838 Premaphotos Wildlife/K.G.Preston-Mafham 839 Jane Goodall Inst./P. Breese 840 Life File/E. Lee 842 J.K. Burras 843 Premaphotos Wildlife/Jean Preston-Mafham 844 (t) A-Z Tourism; (c) Life File/E. Tan 845 (l) Nature Photographers Limited/R. Tidman; (r) Nature Photographers Limited/N.A. Callow 848 (both) Andromeda Oxford Limited 849 Paul Fuqua 850 J. Roles 850-1 J. Roles 852 Life File/E. Lee 855 Biofotos/Heather Angel 856 Nature Photographers Limited/D. Smith 859 (l) Premaphotos Wildlife/K.G. Preston-Mafham; (r) Nature Photographers Limited/E.A Janes FRPS 861 (both) Paul Fuqua 863 (all) Andromeda Oxford Limited

VOLUME 10

869 TRIP/H. Rogers 870 L. Proud 871 G. Bateman 872 Paul Fuqua 873 Nature Photographers/Hugh Miles 874 Life File/Steve Jansen 876 Andromeda Oxford Limited/N. Leggett 877 Andromeda Oxford Limited 879 Texas Highways Magazine 880 (tl) Paul Fuqua; (bl) Premaphotos Wildlife/K.G. Preston-Mafham; (cr)Premaphotos Wildlife/K.G. Preston-Mafham 881

L.M. Stone 882 (l) Premaphotos Wildlife/K.G. Preston-Mafham; (r) Andromeda Oxford Limited 883 St. Bartholomew's Hospital (Science Photo Library) 886 CMSP/M. Pekes 890 (tl) Andromeda Oxford Limited; (bl) Andromeda Oxford Limited; (br) TRIP/NASA 893 TRIP/NASA 894 Science Photo Library/M. Land 895 G.A. Matthews 896 E. Harris 898 Library of Congress 899 (all) Andromeda Oxford Limited 900 Courtesy International Bank for Redevelopment 905 Premaphotos Wildlife/K.G. Preston-Mafham 907 Andromeda Oxford Limited/N. Leggett 910 (both) Andromeda Oxford Limited 911 Life File/C. Field 912 Nature Photographers Limited/Brinsley Burbidge 913 (l) Andromeda Oxford Limited; (r) Suttons Seeds Limited, Devon 914-5 Science Photo Library/Phillippe Plailly 916 Courtesy America Banknotes 918 (l) G. Bateman; (r) Andromeda Oxford Limited 919 (tl) Andromeda Oxford Limited; (b) J. Roles 922 Nature Photographers Limited/Paul Sterry 923 Paul Fuqua 926 (t) Life File/Eddy Tan; (b) Texas Highways Magazine 927 (t) Andromeda Oxford Limited; (bl) Nature Photographers Limited/Paul Sterry; (br) Andromeda Oxford Limited 931 Science Photo Library/David Vaughan 933 Premaphotos Wildlife/K.G. Preston-Mafham 936 TRIP 937 Andromeda Oxford Limited 938 Premaphotos Wildlife/K.G. Preston-Mafham 939 Andromeda Oxford Limited 945 NASA 949 Biofotos/Heather Angel 951 Steven Brown 952 Andromeda Oxford Limited/N. Leggett 953 Paul Fuqua 956 U.S. Coast Guard 958 U.S. Geological Survey 959 Biology Media/Science Photo Library

VOLUME 11

965 (l) Paul Fuqua; (r) U.S. Library International 966 Philips Electronics U.K. Limited 968 Paul Fuqua 969 Biofotos/Heather Angel 970 British Aerospace Defence Limited 970 Bovis Construction Limited 970-1 Vosper Thornycroft (U.K.) Limited 971 (c) Wedgewood; (b) Science Photo Library/David M. Campione 972 Science Photo Library/Joyce Photographics 973 (t) U.S. Air Force; (b) Science Photo Library/Guy Gillette 974 Andromeda Oxford Limited 975 Science Photo Library/Andrew Davies 976 Apple Computer U.K. Limited 978 TRIP 980 (both) Biofotos/Heather Angel 983 (both) Biofotos/Heather Angel 984 Oxford Scientific

Films/Tim Shepherd 985 Paul Fuqua 986 Rockwool Limited 987 Owens-Corning Building Products U.K. Limited 988 Paul Fuqua 989 St. Bartholomew's Hospital/Science Photo Library 995 Olivetti U.K. Limited 996 (l) Andromeda Oxford Limited; (br) Andromeda Oxford Limited; (tl) Mary Evans Picture Library 997 (both r) Ann Ronan Picture Library; (br) Popperfoto 999 Paul Fuqua 1002 Andromeda Oxford Limited 1004 British Steel plc 1005 Science Photo Library/Phillippe Plailly 1006-7 Texas Highways Magazine 1010 Life File/Gina Green 1011 (l) Andromeda Oxford Limited/Nick Leggett; (r) Photo Researchers Inc./Oxford Scientific Films/Renee Lynn 1012 Andromeda Oxford Limited 1013 Paul Fuqua 1015 (bl) NASA; (cr) Sally Hogg 1017 Oxford Scientific Films/Dr. J.A.L. Cooke 1019 TRIP 1021 Library of Congress 1024 Wedgewood 1027 Andromeda Oxford Limited/Nick Leggett 1028 Photo Researchers Inc./Oxford Scientific Films/Melissa Hayesenglish 1029 Steve Brown 1030 Biofotos/Heather Angel 1031 Paul Fuqua 1032 Paul Fuqua 1033 Paul Fuqua 1035 Library of Congress 1036 U.S. Geological Survey 1037 Andromeda Oxford Limited/Nick Leggett 1038 Premaphotos Wildlife/K.G. Preston-Mafham 1040-1 Life File/Emma Lee 1044 Andromeda Oxford Limited 1045 (tr) U.S Geological Survey; (cl) Premaphotos Wildlife/Dr. Rod Preston-Mafham; (br) Andromeda Oxford Limited/Nick Leggett 1046 Library of Congress 1047 Andromeda Oxford Limited/Nick Leggett 1048 (l) Andromeda Oxford Limited/Nick Leggett; (r) Lesley & Roy Adkins Picture Library 1051 (all) Andromeda Oxford Limited 1052 (cl) Premaphotos Wildlife/K.G. Preston-Mafham; (tr) Bettman 1053 Homer Sykes/Andromeda Oxford Limited 1054 J.S. Library International 1056 (l) Paul Fuqua; (r) Bettman

VOLUME 12

1061 (l) Oxford Scientific Films/G.I. Bernard; (cr) ICI Plant Protection Division 1062 (tr) Oxford Scientific Films/Tim Shepherd; (cr) Oxford Scientific Films/D.H. Thompson 1064 Andromeda Oxford Limited/Nick Leggett 1065 Andromeda Oxford Limited/Nick Leggett 1066 Andromeda Oxford Limited 1067 Biofotos/Heather Angel 1068 (cr) Andromeda Oxford Limited/Nick Leggett; (r) NIBSC/Science Photo Library 1069 Life File/Emma Lee 1071 Oxford Scientific Films/John Cooke 1072 Nature Photographers/Paul Sterry 1073 Heather Angel/Biofotos 1077 Paul Fuqua 1080-1 Science Photo Library/Tom McHugh 1083 Courtesy North Carolina Division of Tourism 1084 (l) Life File/Graham Buchan; (tr) Science Photo Library/James Bell; (br) Science Photo Library/Dr. Jeremy Burgess 1085 (l) Andromeda Oxford Limited; (tr) Andromeda Oxford Limited/Eric Crichton; (br) Graham Bateman 1086 (both) Heather Angel/Biofotos 1087 Heather Angel/Biofotos 1088 Heather Angel/Biofotos 1089 Andromeda Oxford Limited 1090 Martin Anderson 1091 Science Photo Library/Magrath Photography 1092 Science Photo Library/Jerry Mason 1094 Paul Fuqua 1095 Premaphotos Wildlife/K.G. Preston-Mafham 1098 Andromeda Oxford Limited 1104 Martin Anderson 1105 (both) Premaphotos/K.G. Preston-Mafham 1106 (t) Heather Angel/Biofotos; (b) Paul Fuqua 1109 Heather Angel/Biofotos 1112 U.S. Forest Service 1112-3 U.S. Forest Service/Jim Hughes 1114 Science Photo Library/Calvin Larsen 1115 U.K. Time/P.R. Unlimited 1117 Andromeda Oxford Limited 1120 Nature Photographers/Roger Tidman 1121 Sally Hogg 1123 Andromeda Oxford Limited 1124 Life File/Jeremy Hoare 1125 Science Photo Library/Institut Pasteur/CNRI 1126 National Park Service 1129 Andromeda Oxford Limited/Nick Leggett 1131 Life File/Tim Fisher 1133 Andromeda Oxford Limited/Eric Crichton 1134 Paul Fuqua 1135 Graham Bateman 1141 National Science Photo/C. Walker 1142 Oxford Scientific Films/Peter Parks 1145 Rand McNally 1146 Rand McNally 1147 Andromeda Oxford Limited 1148 Andromeda Oxford Limited 1151 Life File/NASA 1152 TRIP

VOLUME 13

1157 Nature Photographers/E.A. James 1159 Biofotos/Heather Angel 1160 General Motors 1161 Courtesy Maytag Company 1162 Andromeda Oxford Limited 1165 Paul Fuqua 1166 Premaphotos Wildlife/K.G. Preston-Mafham 1167 Bettman 1168 Science Photo Library/Lowell Georgia 1170 Science Photo Library/Simon Fraser 1171

Philips   1172 Science Photo Library/Hank Morgan   1173 TRIP/H. Rogers   1174 Life File/Nigel Shuttleworth   1176 Science Photo Library/James Stevenson   1177 (l) Premaphotos Wildlife/K.G. Preston-Mafham; (r) Science Photo Library/Adam Hart-Davis   1180 Science Photo Library/Sinclair Stammers   1184 Science Photo Library/Sinclair Stammers   1185 NASA   1187 Paul Fuqua   1189 TRIP/H. Rogers   1190 Viners of Sheffield plc   1190-1 U.S. Department of Energy   1192 Andromeda Oxford Limited   1193 Biofotos/Heather Angel   1194 (both) Paul Fuqua   1195 (both) Paul Fuqua   1196 TRIP   1197 Andromeda Oxford Limited   1198-9 NASA   1201 Seiko U.K. Limited   1202 John Clark   1203 (l) Science Photo Library/A.B. Dowsett; (r) Science Photo Library/Hank Morgan   1204 Andromeda Oxford Limited   1205 (l) Andromeda Oxford Limited; (r) Canon U.K. Limited   1208 Life File/Jeremy Hoare   1210 Science Photo Library/Dr. Jeremy Burgess   1210-11 Life File/Dave Thompson   1212 Life File/Jeremy Hoare   1214 Biofotos/J.M. Pearson   1215 Biofotos/Heather Angel   1216 Paul Fuqua   1217 (t) TRIP; (b) Biofotos/Heather Angel   1218 Premaphotos Wildlife/K.G Preston-Mafham   1220 (both) John Clark   1221 (all) John Clark   1223 Life File/Emma Lee   1224 Courtesy Marquette County Historical Society   1225 (t) TRIP/J. Turco; (b) Oxford Scientific Films/Frank Schneidermeyer   1226 (t) Andromeda Oxford Limited; (b) Oxford Scientific Films/David Thompson   1228 (all) Andromeda Oxford Limited   1230-1 Zefa Pictures   1231 (both) TRIP   1232 TRIP/I. Kolpakova   1233 Andromeda Oxford Limited   1234 Premaphotos Wildlife/K.G. Preston-Mafham   1235 Science Photo Library/Professor P.M. Motta, G. Macchiarelli, S. Anottola   1236 Nature Photographers Limited/Paul Sterry   1237 (l) Life File/Lionel Moss; (r) Science Photo Library/Geoff Tompkinson   1239 (l) Premaphotos Wildlife/K.G. Preston-Mafham;   (r) Nature   Photographers Limited/Geoff du Feu   1242 (l) Oxford Scientific Films/G.I. Bernard; (r) Premaphotos Wildlife/K.G. Preston-Mafham   1243 (l) Biofotos/Heather Angel; (r) Premaphotos Wildlife/K.G. Preston-Mafham 1244 Oxford Scientific Films/Peter Parks 1247 Nature Photographers Limited/E.A. James

VOLUME 14

1253 (both) Andromeda Oxford Limited   1254 TRIP/H. Rogers   1257 NASA   1259 TRIP   (l) Nature Photographers Limited/Paul Sterry; (r) Biofotos/Heather Angel   1261 (l) Andromeda Oxford Limited; (r) Library of Congress   1262 Courtesy Western Union   1263 (l) Courtesy International Masonry Institute; (r) Nature Photographers Limited/Geoff du Feu   1264 Andromeda Oxford Limited   1266 Biofotos/Heather Angel   1268 Life File/Jeremy Hoare   1269 M. Short   1270-1 Biofotos/Heather Angel   1271 Andromeda Oxford Limited   1274 Paul Fuqua   1275 Nature Photographers Limited/Andrew Cleare   1276 (l) Biofotos/Heather Angel; (r) Nature Photographers Limited/Paul Sterry   1282 Ohio Department Natural Resources, Division of Wildlife   1283 Premaphotos Wildlife/Dr. Rod Preston-Mafham   1284 Natural Science Photos   1285 Nature Photographers Limited/Brinsley Burbidge   1286 Life File/Keith Curtis   1288 (l) Nature Photographers Limited/ Christopher Grey-Wilson; (r) Nature Photographers Limited/Paul Sterry   1289 Life File/Lionel Moss 1290 (c) TRIP/V. Kolpakov; (b) TRIP/H. Rogers 1293 TRIP/M. Lee   1295 Science Photo Library/GE Astro Space   1297 NASA   1299 Life File/Aubrey J. Slaughter   1300 NASA   1301 Science Photo Library/Ludek Pesek   1305 Andromeda Oxford Limited   1308 Library of Congress   1309 Courtesy Falconbridge Limited   1311 (l) Nature Photographers Limited/Brinsley Burbidge; (r) Oxford Scientific Films/G.I. Bernard   1314 (both) Paul Fuqua   1315 Paul Fuqua   1316 Marine Nationale 1317 TRIP   1320 Paul Fuqua   1324 Science Photo Library/U.S. Dept. of Energy   1326 Science Photo Library/U.S. Dept. of Energy   1332-3 Andromeda Oxford Limited/Nick Leggett   1332 Andromeda Oxford Limited/Nick Leggett   1333 (l) Paul Fuqua; (r) Andromeda Oxford Limited/Nick Leggett   1334 J.S. Library International   1336 (l) Oxford Scientific Films/G.I. Bernard; (r) Andromeda Oxford Limited 1337 Andromeda Oxford Limited   1338 (l) Life File/Paul Fisher; (r) John Clark   1342 Woods Hole Oceanographic Institution   1343 Survival Anglia Oxford Scientific Films/Marianne Wilding

VOLUME 15

1349 Esso   1351 (all) Andromeda Oxford Limited   1352 J.S. Library International   1355 TRIP/B. Turner   1357 Biofotos/Heather Angel   1358 Biofotos/Heather Angel   1360 (both) Andromeda Oxford Limited   1361 J.S. Library International   1362 Photoresearcher Inc./Oxford Scientific Films/C.K. Lorenz   1363 Oxford Scientific Films/Richard Day   1364 Thurlby Thandar   1365 Biofotos/Heather Angel   1369 Life File/N. Shuttleworth   1370 Life File/David Kampfner   1372 (c) Biofotos/Heather Angel; (b) Life File/Emma Lee   1373 TRIP   1375 (bl) BSIP VEM/Science Photo Library; (tr) Oxford Scientific Films/Survival Anglia   1376 Ohio Department Natural Resources, Division of Wildlife/Ron Keil   1377 Andromeda Oxford Limited   1378 (c) Andromeda Oxford Limited; (b) Nissan Sunderland   1379 Paul Fuqua   1380 Biofotos/Heather Angel   1385 Pulp & Paper   1389 Oxford Scientific Films/Peter Parks   1391 J.S. Library International   1392 Premaphotos Wildlife/K.G. Preston-Mafham   1394 Paul Fuqua   1395 Andromeda Oxford Limited   1396 Library of Congress   1397 Library of Congress   1398 (all) Andromeda Oxford Limited   1399 (tr) Paul Fuqua; (cr) Biofotos/Heather Angel   1400 Andromeda Oxford Limited   1401 (both) Andromeda Oxford Limited   1402 Nature Photographers/Don Smith   1406 Andromeda Oxford Limited   1407 Andromeda Oxford Limited   1409 Life File/Jeremy Hoare   1411 Paul Fuqua   1413 (tl) Oxford Scientific Films/Tim Shepherd; (c) Paul Fuqua; (b) Andromeda Oxford Limited   1414 Paul Fuqua   1415 Life File/Lionel Moss   1416 (tl) Esso; (bl) TRIP/J. Caldow   1416-7 Esso   1418 Paul Fuqua   1419 Andromeda Oxford Limited   1420 Zeneca Corporate Slidebank   1423 (t) Andromeda Oxford Limited; (b) Paul Fuqua   1425 Andromeda Oxford Limited   1427 Biofotos   1429 (all) Andromeda Oxford Limited   1430 TRIP/J. Moscrop   1431 Andromeda Oxford Limited   1432 Nature Photographers/Paul Sterry   1436 Comark   1438 Library of Congress   1440 Oxford Scientific Films/Peter Parks

VOLUME 16

1445 Animals, Animals/Oxford Scientific Films/Breck P. Kent   1446 (both) Paul Fuqua   1447 Science Photo Library/Heine Schneebeli   1448 Andromeda Oxford Limited   1449 (t) Paul Fuqua; (b) Biofotos/Heather Angel   1451 (cl) Biofotos/Heather Angel; (cr) Biofotos/Heather Angel; (bl) Nature Photographers/Andrew Cleave   1452 (l) Andromeda Oxford Limited; (r) Nature Photographers/Paul Sterry   1453 U.S. Department of Energy   1460 Life File/NASA   1461 (l) Science Photo Library/David Parker; (r) Biofotos/Heather Angel   1462 Andromeda Oxford Limited   1463 (all) Andromeda Oxford Limited   1464 (all) Andromeda Oxford Limited   1465 Andromeda Oxford Limited   1466 (both) Andromeda Oxford Limited   1467 (both) Andromeda Oxford Limited   1468 Heather Angel   1469 Andromeda Oxford Limited   1470 Courtesy American Red Cross   1471 (l) Science Photo Library/Roger Rossmeyer, Starlight; (r) London School of Hygiene & Tropical Medicine/Science Photo Library   1472 Science Photo Library/Peter Ryan   1474 (l) Life File/Emma Lee; (r) Life File/Aubrey J. Slaughter   1475 Andromeda Oxford Limited   1477 Johnson Matthey   1480 Biofotos/Heather Angel   1481 Science Photo Library/Lynette Cook   1482 Courtesy Lockheed Aircraft   1484 (both) Andromeda Oxford Limited   1486 (both) Andromeda Oxford Limited   1488 Biofotos/Heather Angel   1489 (t) Oxford Scientific Films/G.I. Bernard; (c) Biofotos/Heather Angel   1490 Andromeda Oxford Limited   1491 TRIP/H. Rogers   1492 Biofotos/Heather Angel   1493 Biofotos/Heather Angel   1495 J.S. Library International   1497 Zedcor/Science Photo Library/James Holmes   1499 (l) Andromeda Oxford Limited; (r) TRIP/H. Rogers   1501 (tl, tr) Andromeda Oxford Limited; (tc) W.W. Schwabe; (bl, br) Biofotos/Heather Angel   1502 (c) Andromeda Oxford Limited; (b) Martin Anderson   1505 Oxford Scientific Films/Georgina Cox   1506 (l) Paul Fuqua; (r) Andromeda Oxford Limited   1508 Life File/Mike Maidment   1509 Paul Fuqua   1512 TRIP/Eric Smith   1513 (l) Diamond Information Centre; (r) Paul Fuqua   1514 Biofotos/Heather Angel   1522 (both) Andromeda Oxford Limited   1530 Oxford Scientific Films/Stan Osolinski   1531 (both) TRIP/H. Rogers   1533 American Petroleum Inst./Standard Oil Co.   1535 J. Michael   1536 (l) Premaphotos Wildlife/R.A. Preston-Mafham; (r) Andromeda Oxford Limited

VOLUME 17

1545 Library of Congress 1546 Library of Congress
1547 St. Bartholomew's Hospital/Science Photo
Library 1548 (tr) Andromeda Oxford Limited; (cr)
J.G. Duckett; (bl) M.C.F. Proctor 1551 Nature
Photographers/Michael Gore 1552 Bovis
Construction 1553 Smithsonian Institution/Science
Photo Library 1554 Biofotos/ Heather Angel 1556
Premaphotos Wildlife/K.G. Preston-Mafham 1561
Science Photo Library/Geoff Tompkinson 1563 M.
Short 1564 (l) John Clark; (r) Premaphotos
Wildlife/K.G. Preston-Mafham 1565 (both)
Biofotos/Heather Angel 1568 TRIP/B. Turner
1569 Rockwell International 1573 TRIP/
B. Turner 1575 Oxford Scientific Films/Frank
Schneidermeyer 1576 U.S. Department of Energy
1577 U.S. Department of Energy 1578-9 U.S.
Department of Energy/Science Photo Library 1580-1
Oxford Scientific Films/Stan Osolinski 1581
NRAO/AUI 1582 TRIP/H. Rogers 1583 (both)
Milwaukee Public Museum 1584 Life File/Emma
Lee 1585 Andromeda Oxford Limited 1590
Amtrak 1590-1 Life File/Fraser Ralston 1592
J.S. Library International 1593 Paul Fuqua 1595
Jenny Fry 1596-7 TRIP/D. Davies 1597 Nature
Photographers Limited/Paul Sterry 1598 Andromeda
Oxford Limited 1600 Andromeda Oxford Limited
1602 Nature Photographers Limited/Paul Sterry
1604 Biofotos/Heather Angel 1608 Andromeda
Oxford Limited 1609 Nature Photographers Ltd
/Roger Tidman 1610 (l) Paul Fuqua; (r) Science
Photo Library/John Sandford 1611 (l) Science Photo
Library/Dr. Jean Lorre; (r) D.M. Keith-Lucas 1612
G.A. Matthews 1616 (t) Paul Fuqua; (b) Nature
Photographers Limited/Andrew Cleave 1621
Premaphotos Wildlife/K.G. Preston-Mafham 1622
Mantis Wildlife Film/Oxford Scientific Films 1627
Biofotos/Heather Angel 1628 J.S. Library
International 1629 TRIP/J. Highet 1630 TRIP/
H. Rogers

VOLUME 18

1641 (all) Andromeda Oxford Limited 1642
International Rice Research Unit 1643 (t) Nature
Photographers Limited/Michael Gore; (c) Food and
Agriculture Organization; (b) International Rice

Research Unit 1644 (t) Science Photo Library/H.
Pol/CNRI; (b) Paul Fuqua 1647 NASA 1648 Paul
Fuqua 1651 (c) Premaphotos Wildlife/Dr. Rod
Preston-Mafham; (b) Biofotos/Heather Angel 1653
(both) Nissan Sunderland 1654 Premaphotos
Wildlife/R.A. Preston-Mafham 1657 TRIP/NASA
1659 NASA 1660 Science Photo Library/Arnold
Fisher 1664 (both) Andromeda Oxford Limited
1667 (l) L. Kasasian; (r) Garrard 1669 Premaphotos
Wildlife/ K.G. Preston-Mafham 1670 Andromeda
Oxford Limited 1671 Andromeda Oxford Limited
1676 (cl) Andromeda Oxford Limited; (tr) Nature
Photographers/Brinsley Burbidge; (cr) Julia Roles; (br)
Julia Roles 1677 (t) Oxford Scientific Films/David
Shale; (b) Nature Photographers/Paul Sterry 1678
Garrard 1679 (t) Premaphotos Wildlife/K.G.
Preston-Mafham; (c) Biofotos/Ian Tait 1680 (t)
Premaphotos Wildlife/K.G. Preston-Mafham; (b)
Biofotos/Heather Angel 1682 TRIP 1683 TRIP
1684-5 NASA 1685 Life File/NASA 1686
Premaphotos Wildlife/K.G. Preston-Mafham 1687
(t) Premaphotos Wildlife/K.G. Preston-Mafham; (b)
Biofotos/Heather Angel 1690 Premaphotos
Wildlife/K.G. Preston-Mafham 1691 Biofotos/
Heather Angel 1693 Zeneca Corporate Slidebank
1694 International Business Machines Corporation
1696 Premaphotos Wildlife/K.G. Preston-Mafham
1698 Nature Photographers/S.C. Bisserot 1699
Nature Photographers/S.C. Bisserot 1702 Nature
Photographers/Michael J. Hammett 1704 Nature
Photographers/S.C. Bisserot 1705 Andromeda
Oxford Limited 1706 (t) Andromeda Oxford
Limited; (b) Nature Photographers/Paul Sterry 1707
(both) Andromeda Oxford Limited 1708
Andromeda Oxford Limited 1712 (t) Andromeda
Oxford Limited; (b) Biofotos/Heather Angel 1714
Nature Photographers/Michael Gore 1717
Premaphotos Wildlife/K.G. Preston-Mafham 1718
Andromeda Oxford Limited 1719 TRIP/H. Rogers
1728 Andromeda Oxford Limited

VOLUME 19

1734 Premaphotos Wildlife/K.G. Preston-Mafham
1735 Intel Corporation 1737 Andromeda Oxford
Limited 1739 British Aerospace Defence Limited
1741 Premaphotos Wildlife/K.G. Preston-Mafham

1743 Paul Fuqua   1750 (both) Life File/Nicola Sutton   1751 (t) Biofotos/Brian Rogers; (c) Biofotos/Heather Angel; (b) Premaphotos Wildlife/Dr. Rod Preston-Mafham   1754 (l) Oxford Scientific Films/Avril Ramage; (r) Paul Fuqua   1757 TRIP/V. Kolpakov   1758 Paul Fuqua   1761 Andromeda Oxford Limited   1762 (c) Biofotos/Heather Angel; (b) Life File/Cliff Threadgold   1763 (l) Andromeda Oxford Limited; (r) Biofotos/Heather Angel 1769 Paul Fuqua   1770 British Sugar   1771 Premaphotos Wildlife/K.G. Preston-Mafham   1772 Andromeda Oxford Limited   1774 Oxford Scientific Films/C.C. Lockwood   1776 TRIP/NASA   1780 Science Photo Library/Mehau Kulyk   1783 Science Photo Library/Tummaso Guicciardini   1784 Andromeda Oxford Limited   1786 Life File/Julia Highet   1787 Life File/Caroline Field   1791 Andromeda Oxford Limited   1793 TRIP/B. Turner   1795 (t) R.B. Gibbons; (b) BASF 1796 Paul Fuqua   1797 Paul Fuqua   1800-1 Survival Anglia/Oxford Scientific Films/Nellaine Price   1808 Oxford Scientific Films/Stephen Dalton   1814 Nature Photographers Limited/David Rae   1815 Premaphotos Wildlife/Cliff Nelson ARPS   1816 Andromeda Oxford Limited   1817 Hal Sommer 1818 Premaphotos Wildlife/K.G. Preston-Mafham 1820 Andromeda Oxford Limited   1823 Nature Photographers Limited/S.C. Bisserot

VOLUME 20

1829 (c) NASA; (b) TRIP   1832 (t) Zefa; (b) Andromeda Oxford Limited   1833 Paul Fuqua   1840 Paul Fuqua   1842 British Steel   1845 The Mansell Collection   1846 Science Photo Library/W & D McIntyre   1847 Andromeda Oxford Limited   1848 Biofotos/Heather Angel   1849 Premaphotos Wildlife/K.G. Preston-Mafham   1850 Paul Fuqua 1851 Julia Roles   1852 (both) Andromeda Oxford Limited   1855 Science Photo Library/Prof. Harold Edgerton   1860 Larry Levine   1861 Premaphotos Wildlife/K.G. Preston-Mafham   1863 (t) British Sugar; (b) Natural Science Photos   1865 Texas Highways Magazine   1866 Premaphotos Wildlife/K.G. Preston-Mafham   1869 (l) Martin Anderson; (r) Paul Fuqua   1870 Jenny Fry   1871 (t) TRIP; (b) Science Photo Library/David Parker   1872 TRIP   1873 British Airways   1874 Martin Anderson

1875 TRIP   1877 Nature Photographers Limited/Andrew Cleave   1879 Nature Photographers Limited/Andrew Cleave   1882 (c) Andromeda Oxford Limited; (b) Martin Anderson   1884 Life File/Dave Thompson   1886 L. Sommerville   1888 Paul Fuqua 1892 Julia Roles   1893 (t) C. Parker; (b) Julia Roles 1894 (c) Courtesy International Business Machines Corporation; (b) Nissan Sunderland   1896-7 Premaphotos Wildlife/K.G. Preston-Mafham   1898 Life File/Ian Richards   1900 (both) Andromeda Oxford Limited   1901 TRIP/H. Rogers   1902 Andromeda Oxford Limited   1905 TRIP/NASA 1906 TRIP   1910 (both) Life File/Jeremy Hoare 1912 Science Photo Library/Adam Hart-Davis   1913 Andromeda Oxford Limited   1914 Derek Hall   1917 Science Photo Library   1918 Nikola Tesla Museum, Belgrade 1919 TRIP

VOLUME 21

1925 (l) D. Harris; (r) Andromeda Oxford Limited 1926 TRIP/J. Wakelin   1927 Paul Fuqua   1928 Wilson & Longbottom   1929 Andromeda Oxford Limited   1931 Hunting Technical Services Ltd 1932-3 Andromeda Oxford Limited   1934 Andromeda Oxford Limited   1935 Andromeda Oxford Limited   1936 Andromeda Oxford Limited 1938 Premaphotos Wildlife/Jean Preston-Mafham 1939 (t) Paul Fuqua; (c) Oxford Scientific Films/David Thompson; (b) Oxford Scientific Films/David Thompson   1943 (l) Life File/Julia Highet; (r) Andromeda Oxford Limited   1944 TRIP/B. Lake   1944-5 National Institutes of Health 1945 Science Photo Library/Andrew Syred   1949 Weed Research Organization   1950 (t) Andromeda Oxford Limited; (c) Andromeda Oxford Limited 1951 (l) Biofotos/Heather Angel; (r) Oxford Scientific Films/Earth Scenes/Breck D. Kent   1953 Oxford Scientific Films/Warren Faidley   1955 Nature Photographers Limited/Paul Sterry   1959 Paul Fuqua 1960 Paul Fuqua   1961 (all) Philips   1962 (t) Philips; (b) Andromeda Oxford Limited   1964 CMSP   1966 (t) Biofotos/Heather Angel; (b) Andromeda Oxford Limited   1967 (both) Elsevier Archives/C.E.Crichton 1968 (tc) A.R. Lovelace; (bl) D. Mabberly; (br) D.M. Keith-Lucas   1971 Paul Fuqua   1972 Biofotos/Heather Angel   1974 Andromeda Oxford Limited

1976 (t) Nature Photographers Limited/Andrew Cleave; (b) Black & Decker   1978-9 Department of Energy   1979 National Power   1980 Paul Fuqua   1982 Biofotos/Heather Angel   1983 L. Somerville   1984 Science Photo Library/Tim Beddow   1985 Nature Photographers Limited/Paul Sterry   1988 TRIP   1993 U.S. Department of Energy   1996 CMSP   1997 English Electric Valve Co. Limited   1998 Nature Photographers Limited   2004 (c) Andromeda Oxford Limited; (b) Andromeda Oxford Limited; (tr) Andromeda Oxford Limited   2005 Life File/Flora Torrance   2008-9 TRIP   2009 NASA   2010 Oxford Scientific Films   2011 Andromeda Oxford Limited   2012 (l) Texas Highways Magazine; (r) Andromeda Oxford Limited   2014 Life File/Dave Thompson   2015 (both) Philips C.E.D. Publicity   2016 (both) Andromeda Oxford Limited

VOLUME 22

2021 (l) Premaphotos Wildlife/K.G. Preston-Mafham; (r) Animals, Animals/Alan G. Nelson   2022 (l) Medical Virology Laboratory/Jeff Ostrow; (r) Oxford Scientific Films/Scott Camazine   2025 Science Photo Library/Hank Morgan   2028 Biofotos/Soames Summerhays   2030 TRIP/J. Wakelin   2030-1 Science Photo Library/David Weintraub   2033 Andromeda Oxford Limited   2034 Goodyear   2038 (bl) Andromeda Oxford Limited; (cr) B. Lenthall; (br) Andromeda Oxford Limited   2042 Nature Photographers Limited/Peter Craig-Cooper   2045 (t) Paul Fuqua; (b) Life File/Emma Lee   2046 Paul Fuqua   2050 TRIP/H. Rogers   2052 TRIP/B. Turner   2054 Life File/Caroline Field   2055 (bl) Nature Photographers Limited/Owen Newman; (cr) Andromeda Oxford Limited; (br) Andromeda Oxford Limited   2057 TRIP/H. Rogers   2058 VPI/Bettman   2059 Library of Congress   2060-1 Premaphotos Wildlife/Mark Preston-Mafham   2063 Andromeda Oxford Limited   2065 (l) J.S. Library International; (r) Biofotos/Heather Angel   2066-7 Premaphotos Wildlife/Dr. Rod Preston-Mafham   2067 Science Photo Library/Martin Bond   2068 Science Photo Library/ESA   2070 Premaphotos Wildlife/Jean Preston-Mafham   2071 (t) Animals, Animals/Michael P. Godoinski; (bl) Andromeda Oxford Limited; (br) Andromeda Oxford Limited   2072 Biofotos/Heather Angel   2073 Premaphotos Wildlife/K.G. Preston-Mafham   2074 NASA/Life File   2075 Life File/Jeremy Hoare   2076 (l) Julia Roles; (r) Science Photo Library/Peter Menzel   2081 (l) Earth Scenes/Oxford Scientific Films/Breck P. Kent; (r) Andromeda Oxford Limited   2082 Life File/Aubrey J. Slaughter   2083 Biofotos/Heather Angel   2085 (tl & tr) Andromeda Oxford Limited; (bl & br) Paul Fuqua   2086-7 TRIP   2088 (t) Biofotos/Heather Angel; (c) Biofotos/Soames Summerhays   2089 Life File/Bob Harris   2091 (l) Menton Wire Limited; (r) Andromeda Oxford Limited   2092 (both) Andromeda Oxford Limited   2094 (c) Nature Photographers Limited/Hugh Clark; (b) Julia Roles   2096 (both) Andromeda Oxford Limited   2097 TRIP/H. Rogers   2099 Courtesy Ivonett Wright Miller   2101 (l) Biofotos/Heather Angel; (r) TRIP/H. Rogers   2102 (cl) Andromeda Oxford Limited; (cr) Andromeda Oxford Limited; (bl) S.R.J. Woodell   2103 Life File/David Kampfner   2105 (l) Nature Photographers Limited/E.A. Janes; (r) Andromeda Oxford Limited   2106 Andreé Abeccus   2109 Galvanisers Association   2111 Julia Roles   2112 Julia Roles